# Make the Grade!

# Understanding **GCSE** Geography
## for AQA Specification A

# Revision Toolkit
## Student Workbook

**Ann Bowen  John Pallister**
**Consultant: Brian Taylor**

www.heinemann.co.uk
✓ Free online support
✓ Useful weblinks
✓ 24 hour online ordering

0845 630 33 33

**Heinemann**
Part of Pearson

# Contents

Introduction                                          iii

Revision Checklist                                    iv

My Revision Planner                                    v

What your GCSE exam papers look like                  vi

## UNIT 1: PHYSICAL GEOGRAPHY

1   The Restless Earth                                 2

2   Rocks, Resources and Scenery                       10

3   Challenge of Weather and Climate                   18

4   Living World                                       26

5   Water on the Land                                  34

6   Ice on the Land                                    42

7   The Coastal Zone                                   50

Skills: Ordnance Survey maps                          58

GradeStudio                                           62

## UNIT 2: HUMAN GEOGRAPHY

8   Population Change                                  64

9   Changing Urban Environments                        72

10  Changing Rural Environments                        80

11  The Development Gap                                 88

12  Globalisation                                      96

13  Tourism                                           104

Skills: Global distribution on maps                  112

GradeStudio                                          114

How well did you do?                                 116

# Welcome to the Revision Toolkit for Understanding GCSE Geography for AQA Specification A

This workbook has been written specially to support you when revising for your GCSE Geography AQA Specification A exams.

## How to use this workbook

This workbook is designed to make revision active! Research shows that actively **doing** revision is much more successful than passively reading through your notes. Using this write-in workbook, you can plan your revision timetable and work your way through a range of interesting activities to help you revise your chosen topics, timing yourself if you want to. You can tick off your topics as you go. Then, you can practise some exam-style questions and see exactly what the examiner is looking for in a top-mark answer. This workbook serves as your own personal record of your revision. It is practical and easy to use, and when used with your textbook, provides a complete revision programme to help you succeed in your exams!

Identify which topics you feel you know well, and which need more work

Colourful activities to make revision more fun!

Practise real exam-style questions and read examiner tips on how to get the top marks

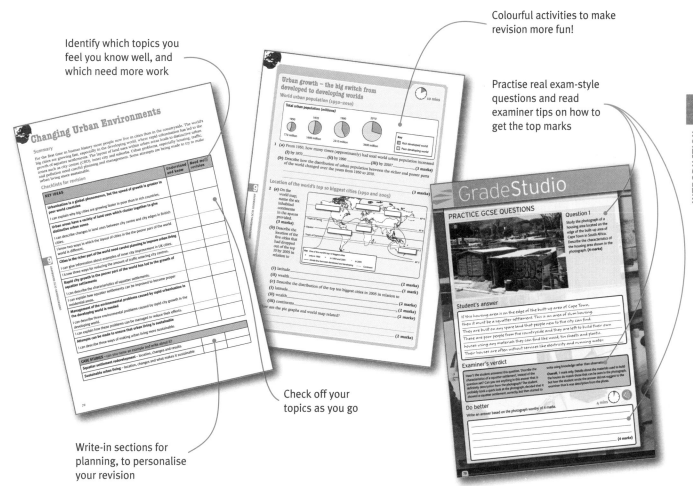

Check off your topics as you go

Write-in sections for planning, to personalise your revision

## Grade Studio  GradeStudio

Grade Studio is designed to help you improve your chances of achieving the best possible grades. You will find Grade Studio activities throughout your workbook with additional resources on your teacher's CD-ROM.

Good luck with your exams. Work hard, make revision active and get the very best results you can!

# Revision Checklist

1 Pick out the topics you are going to revise.

2 Work through this revision workbook. Add YES if you are happy with the topic or NO if you still need more revision.

| | UNIT 1: PHYSICAL GEOGRAPHY | MY TOPICS | YES/NO/DID NOT STUDY |
|---|---|---|---|
| 1 | The Restless Earth | | |
| 2 | Rocks, Resources and Scenery | | |
| 3 | Challenge of Weather and Climate | | |
| 4 | Living World | | |
| 5 | Water on the Land | | |
| 6 | Ice on the Land | | |
| 7 | The Coastal Zone | | |
| | Skills: Ordnance Survey maps | ✓ | |
| | Grade Studio | ✓ | |

| | UNIT 2: HUMAN GEOGRAPHY | MY TOPICS | YES/NO/DID NOT STUDY |
|---|---|---|---|
| 8 | Population Change | | |
| 9 | Changing Urban Environments | | |
| 10 | Changing Rural Environments | | |
| 11 | The Development Gap | | |
| 12 | Globalisation | | |
| 13 | Tourism | | |
| | Skills: Global distribution on maps | ✓ | |
| | Grade Studio | ✓ | |

# Planning your revision:

- The earlier you begin your revision, the easier it will become as the exam approaches.
- Allow time for breaks within and between sessions – revision is normally most effective when undertaken in short, concentrated bursts.
- Set realistic amounts of material to revise during each session to ensure even coverage of the content you will be examined on.

# My Revision Planner

| TOPICS | WEEK 1 | WEEK 2 | WEEK 3 | WEEK 4 | WEEK 5 | WEEK 6 | EXAM DATE |
|---|---|---|---|---|---|---|---|
| The Restless Earth | | | | | | | |
| Rocks, Resources and Scenery | | | | | | | |
| Challenge of Weather and Climate | | | | | | | |
| Living World | | | | | | | |
| Water on the Land | | | | | | | |
| Ice on the Land | | | | | | | |
| The Coastal Zone | | | | | | | |
| Skills: Ordnance Survey maps | | | | | | | |
| Grade Studio | | | | | | | |

| | | | | | | | |
|---|---|---|---|---|---|---|---|
| Population Change | | | | | | | |
| Changing Urban Environments | | | | | | | |
| Changing Rural Environments | | | | | | | |
| The Development Gap | | | | | | | |
| Globalisation | | | | | | | |
| Tourism | | | | | | | |
| Skills: Global distribution on maps | | | | | | | |
| Grade Studio | | | | | | | |

# What your GCSE exam papers look like

## Unit 1: Physical Geography

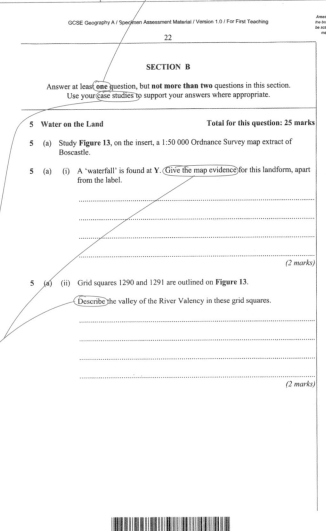

**Time:** ensure that you note how long the exam is and keep this in mind when you are writing your answers. This will help you to keep on track and stop you running out of time.

Read the **instructions** carefully. Before you begin, ensure that you know what is being asked of you. Pay particular attention to how many questions you are required to answer.

Number of questions you have to answer.

Take note of the number of **marks** for each question.

Include **case studies** where appropriate, even when the question itself does not specifically ask for them.

Pay particular attention to the **command words**. Highlight them if necessary.

Centre Number | | | | | Candidate Number | | | | |

| For Examiner's Use | |

Surname

Other Names

Candidate Signature

| Examiner's Initials | |

**AQA** General Certificate of Secondary Education
Higher Tier
Specimen Paper

| Question | Mark |
| --- | --- |
| 1 | |
| 2 | |
| 3 | |
| 4 | |
| 5 | |
| 6 | |
| TOTAL | |

**Geography
(Specification A)**

**40302/H**

**H**

Unit 2: Human Geography

Date: Time

You will need no other materials.
• the insert (enclosed)
• a ruler
You may use a calculator.

**Time allowed**
• 1 hour 30 minutes

**Instructions**
• Use black ink or black ball-point pen.
• Fill in the boxes at the top of this page.
• Answer **three** questions: **one** from **Section A**, **one** from **Section B** and **one** further question from either Section.
• You must answer the questions in the spaces provided. Answers written in margins or on blank pages will not be marked.
• Do all rough work in this book. Cross through any work you do not want to be marked.
• Use your case studies to support your answers where appropriate.

**Information**
• The maximum mark for this paper is 75.
• The marks for questions are shown in brackets.
• You will be marked on your ability to:
  – use an appropriate form and style of writing
  – organise relevant information clearly and coherently
  – use specialist vocabulary where appropriate.

**Time:** ensure that you note how long the exam is and keep this in mind when you are writing your answers. This will help you to keep on track and not run out of time.

Read the **instructions** carefully. Before you begin ensure that you know what is being asked of you. Pay particular attention to how many questions you are required to answer.

Take note of the number of **marks** for each question.

Pay particular attention to the **command words**. Highlight them if necessary.

---

GCSE Geography A / Specimen Assessment Material / Version 1.0 / For First Teaching 2009

Areas outside the box will not be scanned for marking

24

4 (a) (ii) Which continent has the lowest HDI value overall?

.....................................................................................................................
*(1 mark)*

4 (a) (iii) Describe the pattern of the HDI as shown on **Figure 9**.

.....................................................................................................................
.....................................................................................................................
.....................................................................................................................
.....................................................................................................................
.....................................................................................................................
.....................................................................................................................
.....................................................................................................................
.....................................................................................................................
.....................................................................................................................
*(4 marks)*

*(Extra space)* ...................................................................................
.....................................................................................................................
.....................................................................................................................
.....................................................................................................................

4 (a) (iv) Suggest why the HDI is a better guide to development than using Gross National Product per head (GNP per head).

.....................................................................................................................
.....................................................................................................................
.....................................................................................................................
.....................................................................................................................
.....................................................................................................................
.....................................................................................................................
.....................................................................................................................
*(4 marks)*

Paper 2 Higher Tier

Barcode

# The Restless Earth

## Summary

The Restless Earth is all about what happens at plate margins. These are places where plates move, either away from each other (constructive) or towards each other (destructive) or rub past each other (conservative). Their movements result in the formation of fold mountains and volcanoes, and cause earthquakes. All have big effects on people living nearby, but some such as tsunamis and supervolcanoes can have more global effects.

## Checklists for revision

| KEY IDEAS | Understand and know | Need more revision |
|---|---|---|
| **The Earth's crust is unstable** | | |
| I can name several large plates forming the Earth's crust. | | |
| I know the differences between destructive, constructive and conservative plate margins. | | |
| **Major landforms occur at plate margins** | | |
| I can name two landforms at destructive margins and explain their formation. | | |
| I know the main features of the distribution of fold mountains, active volcanoes and earthquakes. | | |
| **Volcanoes are tectonic hazards affecting people** | | |
| I know the differences in appearance and formation between shield volcanoes and composite volcanoes. | | |
| I can give the effects of volcanoes on people using these headings: primary, secondary, positive, negative. | | |
| **Supervolcanoes are volcanoes on a much bigger scale** | | |
| I can state two differences between supervolcanoes and other volcanoes. | | |
| **Earthquakes are tectonic hazards affecting people** | | |
| I know the two different ways of measuring earthquakes. | | |
| I can explain why earthquakes occur at all three types of plate margins. | | |
| I can explain why earthquakes cause more loss of life in poor than in rich countries. | | |

| CASE STUDIES – can you name an example of each and write about it? | | |
|---|---|---|
| **Fold mountains** – formation, human uses and problems for people | | |
| **Volcanic eruption** – cause, effects on people and their responses | | |
| **Earthquakes in both rich and poor countries** – why they occur, effects on people and their responses | | |
| **Tsunami** – cause, places affected, effects on people and their responses | | |

## Quick test

4 mins

1   Name the **three** types of plate margins.

.................................   .................................   .................................   **(3 marks)**

2   Name the **three** landforms (both on land and in the ocean) formed at margins where plates converge and meet.

.................................   .................................   .................................   **(3 marks)**

3   Name **two** different types of volcanic cone.

.................................   .................................   **(2 marks)**

4   Name **two** scales for measuring earthquakes.

.................................   .................................   **(2 marks)**

## Odd one out

6 mins

Circle the odd one out and give a reason.

1   Etna (Sicily)                Mauna Loa (Hawaii)          San Andreas (California)

**Reason:**.................................................................................................................

.................................................................................................................

2   epicentre                   crater                      vent

**Reason:**.................................................................................................................

.................................................................................................................

3   buried by falling masonry   buried under lava and ash   bridges buckle and collapse

**Reason:**.................................................................................................................

.................................................................................................................

4   earthquake-proof buildings  tents, blankets and water   sniffer dogs and lifting gear

**Reason:**.................................................................................................................

# Label the world maps

## Plate margins

**1** Shade or colour in the following plate margins on the world map and complete the key.

| one conservative margin | two constructive margins | three destructive margins |
|---|---|---|

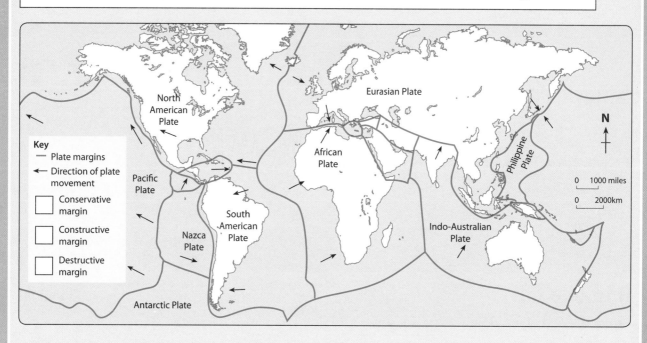

## Fold mountains and ocean trenches

**2 (a)** On the map, show the courses of the plate margins responsible for the formation of fold mountains and ocean trenches.

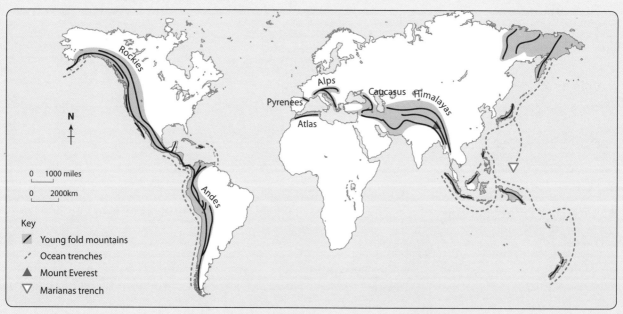

**(b)** What is the main type of plate margin? ........................................................................

**(c)** Why is this type of plate margin best for the formation of fold mountains and ocean trenches?

........................................................................................................................................

........................................................................................................................................

# Label and complete

**1** Add these labels to the diagrams where appropriate:

| | | | | | |
|---|---|---|---|---|---|
| mantle | continent | ocean | oceanic plate | continental plate | ocean trench |
| subduction zone | mid-oceanic ridge | fold mountain range | shield volcano | composite volcano | |

**2** Then, fill in the information on the right of each diagram.

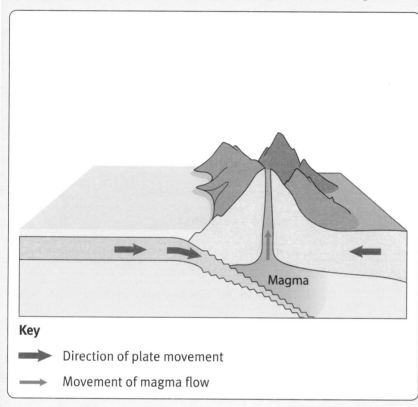

Magma

**Key**

→ Direction of plate movement

→ Movement of magma flow

Type of margin:

Named examples of plates:

Named examples of landforms:

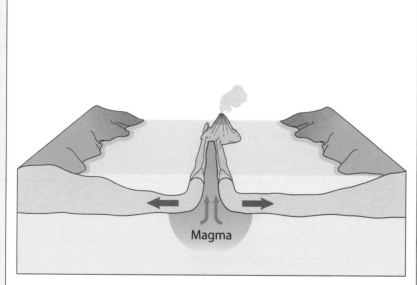

Magma

**Key**

→ Direction of plate movement

→ Movement of magma flow

Type of margin:

Named examples of plates:

Named examples of landforms:

## VOLCANIC ERUPTION

Name of volcano ......................................................

Location ......................................................

Type of volcanic cone ......................................................

**Cause**

Type of plate boundary ......................................................

Names of plates ......................................................

**Effects of eruption**

Primary ......................................................

Secondary ......................................................

Effects/impacts – positive or negative or both?

......................................................

......................................................

**People's responses**

Immediate ......................................................

......................................................

Long term (months or years) ......................................................

......................................................

## TSUNAMI

Name and date ......................................................

Places affected ......................................................

**Cause**

Strength of earthquake ......................................................

Names of plates ......................................................

**Effects**

Secondary effects of earthquake

......................................................

......................................................

Places close to the epicentre ......................................................

Places further away ......................................................

Maximum distance affected ............................... km

**People's responses**

Immediate ......................................................

......................................................

Long term (months or years) ......................................................

......................................................

## EARTHQUAKE IN A RICH PART OF THE WORLD

Place and date ......................................................

Richter scale ......................................................

**Cause**

Type of plate boundary ......................................................

Names of plates ......................................................

**Effects of earthquake**

Primary ......................................................

Secondary ......................................................

Effects/impacts – high or low?

......................................................

......................................................

Reasons ......................................................

**People's responses**

Immediate ......................................................

......................................................

Long term (months or years) ......................................................

......................................................

## EARTHQUAKE IN A POORER AREA

Place and date ......................................................

Richter scale ......................................................

**Cause**

Type of plate boundary ......................................................

Names of plates ......................................................

**Effects of earthquake**

Primary ......................................................

Secondary ......................................................

Effects/impacts – high or low?

......................................................

......................................................

Reasons ......................................................

**People's responses**

Immediate ......................................................

......................................................

Long term (months or years) ......................................................

......................................................

# GradeStudio

## EXAMINATION TECHNIQUE

**10 mins**

**1** Explain the formation of fold mountains. **(4 marks)**

**For a full mark answer, arrange these explanatory statements in the most logical order.**

> **A** two plates move towards each other
>
> **B** sedimentary rocks are upfolded into high mountains
>
> **C** sediments are deposited on the sea bed where they accumulate
>
> **D** sediments compressed into rock in a geosyncline
>
> **E** rivers carry sediments from the land
>
> **F** compression from continued plate movements crumple up the sediments

**2** Give reasons why strong earthquakes occur at destructive plate margins. **(4 marks)**

**Cross out and correct the mistake in each sentence below to make it a correct, full mark answer.**

> Two plates moving apart from each other collide with great force. The lighter
> ocean crust sinks below the heavier continental crust. Great stresses build up in
> the subduction zone as the continental plate sinks down below the oceanic plate.
> Energy builds up which is released from time to time below the ground surface as the
> epicentre of the earthquake. Surface shock waves radiate out in all directions from
> the focus. These increase in strength with distance from the centre.

**3(a)** Describe the characteristics of a shield volcano. **(4 marks)**

**(b)** Explain its formation. **(4 marks)**

**Identify the four descriptive statements that are needed for a full mark answer to question 3(a) and write them out below. Then explain the formation of a shield volcano to a partner using the remaining statements.**

> **A** built of basic lava
>
> **B** basic lava flows long distances forming the wide base
>
> **C** basic lava is runny which is why the sides are gentle
>
> **D** made of lava only
>
> **E** magma rises up from the mantle
>
> **F** eruptions are frequent and usually non-violent
>
> **G** two plates move apart at a constructive margin
>
> **H** cone with gentle slopes and wide base
>
> **I** some of the magma is forced out to the surface through a vent
>
> **J** lava pours out on the surface through the crater

## PRACTICE GCSE QUESTIONS

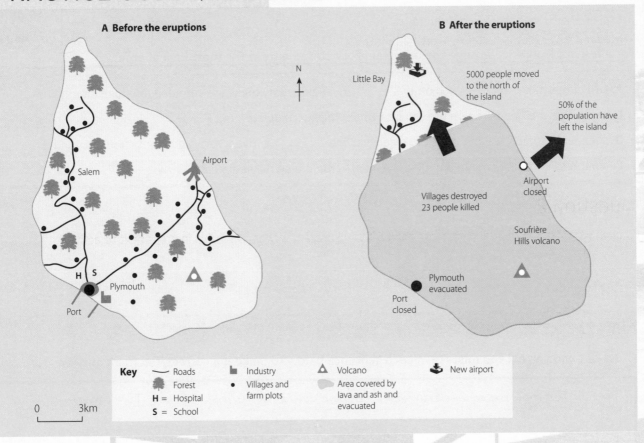

**Figure 1** Montserrat before and after the eruptions in 1995 and 1997.

## Question 1

Use maps A and B in **Figure 1** to describe how the land and land uses in Montserrat were changed by the eruptions of the Soufrière Hills volcano in 1995 and 1997. **(3 marks)**

## Student's answer

The land and land uses were changed a lot by the eruptions of the Soufrière Hills volcano in 1995 and 1997.[1] The big change was the large area in brown shading for the large amount of lava and ash which covered a lot of the land. The Airport is closed, villages were destroyed, Plymouth was evacuated and its port is closed.[2] Many farm plots shown in A were covered by volcanic lava and ash, also the forests.[3]

## Examiner's verdict

1 No marks are ever given for repeating the question.

2 Beginning to answer the question, although the student only refers to map B instead of using both maps A and B to describe how the land and land uses were changed.

3 This last sentence is the most relevant and useful; the candidate is now answering the question, but then stops

because all the lines have been filled. It would have been better if the candidate had not written the first sentence.

**Overall**, this answer is worth at least 1 mark, perhaps 2, but definitely not all 3 marks.

## Do better

Write an answer that is certainly worth all 3 marks.

4 mins

## Question 2

Explain why, despite the dangers, more than 500 million people worldwide live in areas next to active volcanoes.   **(4 marks)**

## Student's answer

Active volcanoes have many advantages like

good soils and hot land,

lots of tourists,

hot springs and geysers as well as useful minerals.

Also people know when a volcano is going to become active again.

## Examiner's verdict

The candidate is giving advantages for people who live in areas next to active volcanoes. Also relevant is the suggestion (or hint) that volcanic eruptions might be predictable. But the layout is not good. Listing is not an acceptable way of answering questions with the command words 'Explain why'. Some phrases used are too vague like 'good soils' and 'useful minerals'; others are not explained such as why volcanic areas attract tourists or details about warning signs before a volcano erupts again.

**Overall**, only a Level 1 performance worth 1 or 2 marks. This student's answer is grade D/E standard.

## Do better

Write a top Level 2 answer worth 4 marks.

5 mins

HOW WELL DID YOU DO? SEE PAGE 116

# Rocks, Resources and Scenery

## Summary

The British Isles is made from three types of rock – igneous, sedimentary and metamorphic. They took hundreds of millions of years to form. Different types of weathering are breaking the rocks into smaller pieces. These small pieces are then transported by rivers into the sea, as part of the Earth's rock cycle. Rocks like granite, chalk, clay and Carboniferous limestone produce their own distinctive landforms and landscapes. They provide valuable resources for people to use. However, quarrying these rocks leads to conflict and debate.

## Checklists for revision

| KEY IDEAS | Understand and know | Need more revision |
|---|---|---|
| **The geological timescale is measured in millions of years** | | |
| I know the positions of rocks such as granite, limestone and chalk on the geological timescale. | | |
| **Rocks belong to three groups and are linked to the rock cycle** | | |
| I can name the three groups of rocks and give examples of each type. | | |
| I know the differences between rocks in the north-west and south-east of Britain. | | |
| I understand how the rock cycle works. | | |
| **Rocks are broken down by different types of weathering** | | |
| I can explain differences between mechanical, biological and chemical weathering. | | |
| **Different rocks create contrasting landforms and landscapes** | | |
| I can describe granite landscapes and explain how tors are formed. | | |
| I can describe features of Carboniferous limestone scenery and explain how limestone solution leads to their formation. | | |
| I can describe the features of a chalk escarpment and explain why chalk and clay landscapes are so different. | | |
| **Rocks provide useful resources for people** | | |
| I know the main economic uses of granite, limestone and chalk rocks. | | |
| I understand why opportunities for farming and tourism vary between different rock types. | | |
| I can explain why quarrying causes local conflict and debate, and needs to be carefully managed. | | |

| CASE STUDIES – can you name an example and write about it? | | |
|---|---|---|
| **One rock type for each of the following:** <br> **farming** – opportunities and limitations | | |
| **aquifer** – advantages and limitations for water supply | | |
| **tourism** – opportunities, benefits and costs | | |
| **A working quarry** – advantages and disadvantages | | |
| **Management of a quarry** – ways to reduce impact during and after use | | |

# Quick test

5 mins

## Rocks (10 marks)

| chalk | clay | granite | limestone |
|---|---|---|---|

**1** Fill in the rock type from those in the box above.

**(a)** An igneous rock .................................................

**(b)** The type of rock formed in the Carboniferous period .................................................

**(c)** Provides an aquifer water supply in south-east England .................................................

**(d)** Forms upland scenery with surface bogs .................................................

**(e)** Forms wet lowland prone to flooding .................................................

**2** Give the type of rock found at the following locations in England from those in the box above.

**(a)** Dartmoor and Land's End .................................................

**(b)** Peak District and Yorkshire Dales .................................................

**(c)** London Basin .................................................

**(d)** Chilterns and South Downs .................................................

**(e)** Cliffs at Dover .................................................

## Weathering (5 marks)

| biological | chemical | mechanical |
|---|---|---|

**3** Fill in the weathering type from those in the box above.

**(a)** Freeze–thaw breaks up rock into scree .................................................

**(b)** Tree roots widen joints in limestone rock .................................................

**(c)** Heating and cooling peels off surface layers of rock .................................................

**(d)** Limestone rock dissolves in rain that is slightly acid .................................................

**(e)** Organic acids released by vegetation rot rocks .................................................

## Rock cycle (5 marks)

**Mountain building**

| igneous | metamorphic | sedimentary |
|---|---|---|

**4 (a)** Fill in the rock group from those in the box above.

**(i)** Old land sediments upfolded again into mountains .................................................

**(ii)** New molten materials from inside the Earth .................................................

**(iii)** Altered by heat and pressure of Earth's movements .................................................

**Surface rocks are weathered, eroded and transported**

**(b)** Circle the correct definition of weathering.

Breakdown of rock at or            Wearing away of the surface
near the surface in situ            by rivers, ice and sea

**Materials from the land are compacted into rock on the sea bed.**

**(c)** Name the rock group formed. .................................................

The cycle then begins again with new mountain building.

# Rocks, landscapes and landforms – label and complete

**10 mins**

## Granite scenery

1 On the diagram

    **(a)** name the landform

    **(b)** label the rock joints.

2 **(a)** Name the main type of weathering which forms this landform.

    ..................................................

    **(b)** Why does this landform form where rock joints are wide apart?

    ..................................................

    ..................................................

    ..................................................

## Carboniferous limestone scenery

3 On the diagram

    **(a)** shade in the layer of Carboniferous limestone rock **(i)** underground and **(ii)** where it outcrops on the surface.

    **(b)** label one example of a swallow hole, a gorge, a dry valley and a cavern.

4 **(a)** Describe the course of the stream marked S.

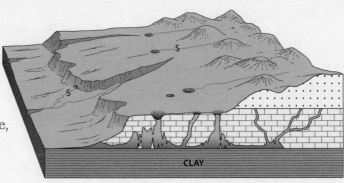

CLAY

..................................................

    **(b)** Why does it take this course?.................

## Chalk and clay scenery

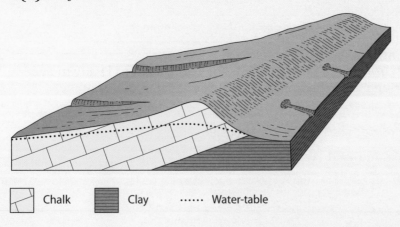

Chalk     Clay    ...... Water-table

5 On the diagram

    **(a)** label dip slope, scarp slope, dry valley and spring

    **(b)** shade in where the chalk rock is saturated.

6 Could the springs and streams they supply ever run dry?

..................................................

..................................................

# Quarrying – advantages and disadvantages

 10 mins

1 Quarrying rocks leads to conflict and debate. Some of the advantages and disadvantages of quarrying are given in the box below. Use them to complete the diagrams below.

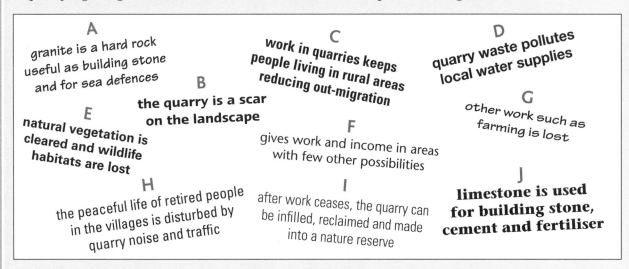

**A** granite is a hard rock useful as building stone and for sea defences

**B** the quarry is a scar on the landscape

**C** work in quarries keeps people living in rural areas reducing out-migration

**D** quarry waste pollutes local water supplies

**E** natural vegetation is cleared and wildlife habitats are lost

**F** gives work and income in areas with few other possibilities

**G** other work such as farming is lost

**H** the peaceful life of retired people in the villages is disturbed by quarry noise and traffic

**I** after work ceases, the quarry can be infilled, reclaimed and made into a nature reserve

**J** limestone is used for building stone, cement and fertiliser

Write the corresponding letter in the correct box. There will be at least one letter in each box.

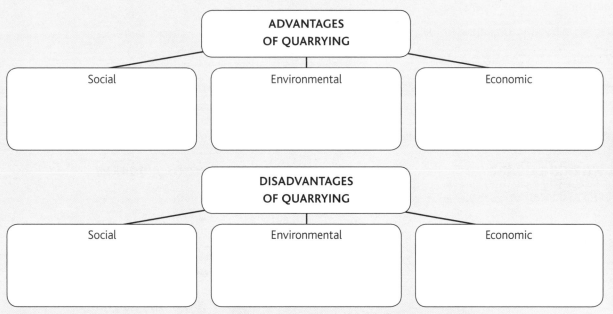

**ADVANTAGES OF QUARRYING**

| Social | Environmental | Economic |

**DISADVANTAGES OF QUARRYING**

| Social | Environmental | Economic |

2 Out of economic, social and environmental, which one is the strongest for **(i)** advantages and **(ii)** disadvantages of quarrying? Explain your choices. You are free to use other advantages and disadvantages of quarrying not stated here in your explanation.

**(i)** Choice for advantages

**(ii)** Choice for disadvantages

**Why?**

**Why?**

## ROCK TYPE

**Example: Carboniferous limestone**

Locations in UK ..................................................................................................................

**Economic uses**

For building stone and materials ........................................................................................

Advantages ........................................................................................................................

**Water supply**

Aquifer or surface? ..................................... How useful? (advantages/disadvantages) ..........

..............................................................................................................................................

**Farming**

Types of farming ................................................................................................................

Opportunities (advantages) ................................................................................................

Limitations ........................................................................................................................

**Tourism**

Opportunities (natural attractions) ....................................................................................

Benefits ............................................................................................................................

Costs ................................................................................................................................

**QUARRY CASE STUDIES** (either two different quarries, or the same quarry used for both)

### A WORKING QUARRY

Name and location ................................................

....................................................................................

**Advantages**

Economic ..............................................................

....................................................................................

Social ....................................................................

....................................................................................

Environmental (if any) ..........................................

**Disadvantages**

Economic ..............................................................

Social ....................................................................

....................................................................................

Environmental ......................................................

**Overall assessment** – do the advantages outweigh the disadvantages?

....................................................................................

### MANAGEMENT OF A QUARRY

Name and location ................................................

....................................................................................

**Strategies – ways to reduce impact**

During extraction ..................................................

....................................................................................

....................................................................................

....................................................................................

When quarry work stops ........................................

....................................................................................

....................................................................................

**Overall assessment** – How effective are the strategies at reducing the impact?

....................................................................................

## EXAMINATION TECHNIQUE

**10 mins**

**1** Describe how the relief and drainage of chalk and clay landscapes are different. **(4 marks)**

**Cross out and correct the mistake(s) in each sentence to make this a correct, full mark answer.**

> The relief of a chalk escarpment is made up of a gentle scarp slope and a steep dip slope. The dip slope is cut by steep sided U-shaped dry valleys, whereas clay forms wide areas of hilly land known as clay valleys. There is little surface drainage on the chalk because the rock is impermeable. Rainwater seeps underground to form underground water stores in springs. Clay is different because the rock is permeable and has many rivers flowing across its surface. Where chalk and clay meet at the bottom of slopes, wells provide a natural water supply of water from underground to feed surface streams.

**2** Give reasons why there are few surface rivers in areas of Carboniferous limestone rocks. **(4 marks)**

**From the box, choose the six statements needed to answer this question. In the space provided, arrange them in a logical order for a correct answer worth all 4 marks.**

| | |
|---|---|
| A | Surface joints are widened by solution into swallow holes down which rivers flow underground. |
| B | Rainwater and carbon dioxide combine to form carbonic acid which slowly dissolves the rock. |
| C | This type of limestone rock has many lines of weakness (bedding planes and joints). |
| D | Underground water reaches the surface again through wells and springs. |
| E | The rock is permeable because it is full of holes down which water can pass. |
| F | Spaces in the rock are filled with water which increases the height of the water table. |
| G | More water sinks down holes in the surface as lines of weakness are widened further by solution. |
| H | After heavy rain water can flow on the surface again in temporary streams called bournes. |
| I | Surface water seeps between the pores in the rock to form an underground aquifer. |
| J | These make the rock vulnerable to attack from chemical weathering and limestone solution. |

# GradeStudio

## PRACTICE GCSE QUESTIONS

Photograph A

### Question 1

Photograph A shows an area of chalk and clay rocks in Sussex in south-east England.

Describe the variations in landscape features and land uses shown in Photograph A.
**(4 marks)**

## Student's answer

The main difference that I can see on photo A is the one between the quite steep slope in the front of the picture and the flatter and lower land further away in the top of the [1] photo. There looks to be a path coming up the steep slope where the grass has been trampled down by people. Whereas in the background there are fields of corn which look [2] ripe and ready to be combined. There are only a few trees, but no forests. Nor can I see any grazing animals or marshy areas. I cannot see much sign of settlements and farms [3] which you would expect to see in a country area like this.

## Examiner's verdict

There are good and bad things throughout this answer.

1 Good – the student recognises the main landscape variation between the steep chalk scarp slope and flat clay vale, and attempts to indicate where they are located.

   Bad – by not stating landform names, the student isn't using the best geographical language.

2 Good – the focus is on the variation in land use between grass on the chalk and crop growing on the lowlands.

   Bad – again there is a lack of use of geographical language

such as pasture and arable.

3 Good – the student seems to understand what is meant by the term land uses and knows what to look for.

   Bad – there are no marks for stating what cannot be seen, what is not there; you can go on forever doing this. If there are trees to be seen, describe where they are found, how many there are, etc.

   **Overall**, on the borderline between Level 1 and Level 2, worth at least 2 marks, possibly 3, which makes it a grade C standard answer.

## Do better

On the top of page 17, write an answer in your own style worth all 4 marks.

4 mins

## Question 2

Describe and explain variations in the opportunities and limitations for farming between different rock types in the UK.   **(6 marks)**

## Student's answer

1 My example of a rock type in the UK is granite.

2 This rocks outcrops in Dartmoor on the moors of the South West.

3 Much of the land is covered by heather and bog.

4 These make it useless for farming other than for sheep.

5 There are also the Dartmoor ponies.

6 The best farmland is around the edges of the uplands with more fertile soils.

7 Dairy farming is the main type of farming because of plenty of rain and good grass growth.

## Examiner's verdict

Definitely only a Level 1 response, worth a maximum of 2 marks. As only one type of rock referred to, it is impossible to show variations between rock types. The layout is terrible and the numbered points are not even separate points. A grade E/F standard of answer.

## Do better

Write a top Level 3 answer worth all 6 marks.

**6 mins**

HOW WELL DID YOU DO? SEE PAGE 116

# Challenge of Weather and Climate

## Summary

The UK's climate is summarised as cool and wet, but with considerable variations within the UK. Depressions and anticyclones bring contrasting types of weather. Some people believe that extreme weather events, such as heavy rainfall leading to floods, are becoming more frequent. This forms part of the wider debate about global warming; predicted consequences require local, national and international responses. Tropical revolving storms are one major climate hazard; peoples' responses to them vary between rich and poor countries.

## Checklists for revision

| KEY IDEAS | Understand and know | Need more revision |
|---|---|---|
| **The characteristics of the UK climate can be explained by its global position, but there are variations within the UK** | | |
| I can state the main characteristics of the UK's climate. | | |
| I can describe the variations in climate within the UK, between North and South and between West and East. | | |
| I know how and why temperatures vary within the UK. | | |
| **Depressions and anticyclones are dominant influences on UK weather and bring contrasting weather** | | |
| I can describe and explain weather changes as a frontal depression moves over the UK. | | |
| I know how and why anticyclonic weather in the UK differs between summer and winter. | | |
| **Extreme weather events are increasing in the UK with negative and positive effects on people** | | |
| I can write about an example of an extreme weather event in the UK (such as a drought, flood or great storm). | | |
| **There is debate about causes and likely consequences of global climate change, and how people need to respond** | | |
| I can give some of the possible causes and consequences of global warming. | | |
| I can name and describe some of the international attempts to respond to the threat of global warming. | | |
| I can state examples of local responses to the threat of global climate change from high carbon dioxide emissions. | | |
| **Tropical revolving storms are a major climate hazard with different effects and responses between rich and poor** | | |
| I understand why tropical storms such as cyclones and hurricanes cause so much damage and destruction. | | |

| CASE STUDIES – can you name an example of each and write about it? | | |
|---|---|---|
| **An extreme weather event in the UK** – areas affected, impacts, responses and plans for the future | | |
| **A tropical storm** – location, causes, effects and responses | | |

## Quick test

**10 mins**

**1**

| north | south | west | east |

Choose one of the locations above for each of the statements below about the UK's climate.

**(a)** wettest .................................................... **(b)** driest ....................................................

**(c)** warmest in winter .................................... **(d)** warmest in summer ..........................

**(e)** sunniest ..............................................

**(5 marks)**

**2**

| high/anticyclone | low/depression |

Choose the pressure system most likely to cause these types of weather or weather events in the UK.

**(a)** winter storm .......................................... **(b)** summer heatwave ..............................

**(c)** floods .................................................... **(d)** mild winters ......................................

**(e)** night fogs .............................................. **(f)** summer drought ................................

**(g)** big winter freeze .................................. **(h)** above average rainfall ....................

**(4 marks)**

**3**

| northern hemisphere | polar | southern hemisphere | temperate | tropical |

Choose the world zone from the box above which matches each of these ranges of latitude.

**(a)** 0 – 30º N & S ........................................ **(b)** 0 – 90º N ..........................................

**(c)** 30 – 60º N & S ...................................... **(d)** 60 – 90 º N & S ................................

**(e)** 0 – 90º S ..............................................

**(2 marks)**

**4**

| altitude | distance from the sea | latitude | pressure system | prevailing wind |

Which of the climate factors in the box above best explains each of the following.

**(a)** high and low rates of insolation causing global temperature variations ........................

**(b)** decrease in temperature of 1ºC per 160 metre increase in height ..............................

**(c)** maritime or continental climate ................................................................

**(d)** wet or dry weather ................................................................

**(e)** the Scilly Isles and western Scottish islands having the mildest winters in the UK

........................................ and ........................................

**(5 marks)**

**5** Give the similarities and differences between a UK frontal depression and a tropical storm.

|  | Similarities | Differences |
|---|---|---|
| Pressure |  |  |
| Sequence of weather |  |  |

**(4 marks)**

# Label and complete

**10 mins**

## Anticyclones

**1 (a)** On **Figure 1 (i)** label the movements of air shown by the arrows; **(ii)** mark 'C' for the anticyclone's centre.

**(b)** Explain why:

**(i)** highest pressure is where you have marked 'C'

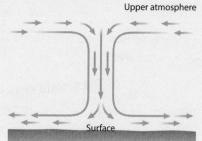

Upper atmosphere

Surface

**Figure 1** What happens in an anticyclone

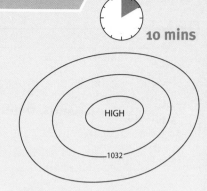

HIGH

1032

**Figure 2** How an anticyclone looks on a weather map

**(ii)** anticyclonic weather is usually dry

**(iii)** clear skies lead to hot weather in summer but cold weather in winter.

**(c)** On **Figure 2**, number the remaining isobars for a pressure interval of 4mbs.

## Frontal depressions

**2 (a)** On **Figure 3**

**(i)** name the warm sector **(ii)** label three different types of cloud and **(iii)** shade in the two areas where rain is most likely.

**(b)** On **Figure 4**, number the isobars for a pressure interval of 4mbs, and name the fronts.

**(c)** Cross out the wrong answers in the passage below where a choice of answer is given.

Cold front

Warm front

Surface

**Figure 3** Cross-section of a frontal depression

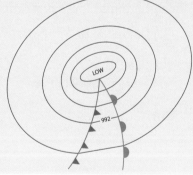

LOW

992

**Figure 4** How a frontral depression looks on a weather map

The approach of a depression from the **Atlantic Ocean/North Sea** is indicated by **falling/rising** air pressure and a **dense mass/thin film** of **high/low cloud**. Over the next few hours, the cloud becomes **denser and lower/thinner and taller** until it becomes **high/thick** enough for rain to fall from it. The rain stops once the **cold/warm** front passes through and temperatures **decrease/increase** by a few degrees in the warm sector. The centre of the depression continues to move east. Towards the rear of the warm sector, **cold/warm** air thrusts forward and lifts the **cold/warm** air off the ground. This happens at the **cold/warm** front. Towering **cirrus/cumulus** clouds develop from which heavy rain often falls. Air pressure **rises/falls**. As the cold air in the rear of the depression is warmed over its long sea journey, it triggers off **heavy showers/long periods of rain** on west-facing coasts of the UK.

# Threat of global climate change

**10 mins**

higher flood risk in low lying coastal areas such as Netherlands, Bangladesh, Maldives

enhanced greenhouse effect from human $CO_2$ emissions

Kyoto climate change conference 1997 targets set for $CO_2$ reductions in rich countries

deforestation; cutting down rainforests for logging, farming and mining

average world temperatures 1900 14.25°C; 2000 14.85°C

mountain glaciers retreating Arctic ice thinning and melting

energy efficiencies better insulation of homes

government targets for increased renewables use EU forcing national governments to respond

sea levels rising 18cms higher than 100 years ago

more frequent extreme weather events more intense and lasting longer

great use of fossil fuels in power stations and for transport

less snowfall during UK winters less cold UK winters than in the 1960s

1 Rearrange the twelve pieces of information about global warming under these key headings for the study of climate change. (Numbers under each of the four key headings are equal.)

**Evidence for global warming**

...........................................................................................................................................................

...........................................................................................................................................................

**Causes**

...........................................................................................................................................................

...........................................................................................................................................................

**Consequences**

...........................................................................................................................................................

...........................................................................................................................................................

**Responses**
- International .......................................................................................................................................
- National ............................................................................................................................................
- Local .................................................................................................................................................

2 State one reason why responses have been slower than environmentalists would have liked:

(a) on an international level ...............................................................................................................

(b) on a national level .......................................................................................................................

(c) on a local level .............................................................................................................................

# Know your case studies: key facts

## TROPICAL STORM IN POOR COUNTRY

Date ...........................................................................

Name and location ..................................................

**Causes**

...........................................................................................

...........................................................................................

**Effects**

Economic .................................................................

...........................................................................................

Social .......................................................................

...........................................................................................

Environmental ........................................................

...........................................................................................

Similarities/differences from the other ................

...........................................................................................

...........................................................................................

**Responses**

Short-term ...............................................................

...........................................................................................

Long-term ................................................................

...........................................................................................

...........................................................................................

## TROPICAL STORM IN RICH COUNTRY

Date ...........................................................................

Name and location ..................................................

**Causes**

...........................................................................................

...........................................................................................

**Effects**

Economic .................................................................

...........................................................................................

Social .......................................................................

...........................................................................................

Environmental ........................................................

...........................................................................................

Similarities/differences from the other ................

...........................................................................................

...........................................................................................

**Responses**

Short-term ...............................................................

...........................................................................................

Long-term ................................................................

...........................................................................................

...........................................................................................

## EXTREME WEATHER EVENT IN THE UK

Date ....................................... Areas affected .................................................

Causes ...............................................................................................................

...........................................................................................................................

**Impacts**

Economic (agriculture, transport, etc.) ..................................................................

...........................................................................................................................

Social (people's homes, lives, health) ...................................................................

...........................................................................................................................

**Responses**

...........................................................................................................................

...........................................................................................................................

Plans for the future .............................................................................................

...........................................................................................................................

# EXAMINATION TECHNIQUE

**1(a)** Describe the main characteristics of tropical storms. **(3 marks)**

**(b)** Explain how and why they are formed. **(5 marks)**

**All the statements needed for full mark exam answers to the two parts of this question are written below. Choose the statements needed for each answer. Five are needed for (a) and seven for (b). Then write them out in the correct order for full mark GCSE answers. Why is good organisation very important when explaining formation?**

> a deep centre of low pressure is created
>
> air is sucked down in the centre to form an eye of calm and dry in the centre
>
> air is sucked in to replace the rising air
>
> hurricane force winds up to or over 200km/hr
>
> hot sea water (27°C+) heats up air above
>
> island countries in the Caribbean and East Asia are hit most
>
> rising currents of air form towering cumulo-nimbus clouds from which heavy rain falls
>
> the weather sequence is windy and wet, calm and dry in the eye, then windy and wet again
>
> they form over sea surfaces in the tropics in late summer and autumn
>
> warm moist sea air starts to rise in convection currents
>
> winds increase to hurricane force as the pressure gradient increases
>
> very deep area of low pressure below 960mbs

**(a)** Describe the main characteristics of tropical storms.

................................................................................................................................................................
................................................................................................................................................................
................................................................................................................................................................
................................................................................................................................................................
................................................................................................................................................................
........................................................................................................................................ **(3 marks)**

**(b)** Explain how and why they are formed.

................................................................................................................................................................
................................................................................................................................................................
................................................................................................................................................................
................................................................................................................................................................
................................................................................................................................................................
................................................................................................................................................................
................................................................................................................................................................
................................................................................................................................................................
........................................................................................................................................ **(5 marks)**

# GradeStudio

## GCSE EXAM QUESTIONS

### Question 1

Study the climate data below for Stornoway (location NW Scotland, latitude 58°N, height 3m) and London (location SE England, latitude 51°N, height 5m).

**(a)** Describe the characteristics of the climate of Stornoway. **(4 marks)**

| | J | F | M | A | M | J | J | A | S | O | N | D |
|---|---|---|---|---|---|---|---|---|---|---|---|---|
| **Stornoway** | | | | | | | | | | | | |
| Temperature (°C) | 4 | 4 | 5 | 7 | 9 | 11 | 13 | 13 | 11 | 9 | 6 | 5 |
| Precipitation (mm) | 125 | 86 | 86 | 69 | 56 | 63 | 76 | 86 | 109 | 129 | 123 | 125 |
| **London** | | | | | | | | | | | | |
| Temperature (°C) | 4 | 5 | 7 | 10 | 13 | 15 | 18 | 17 | 15 | 11 | 8 | 5 |
| Precipitation (mm) | 54 | 40 | 37 | 37 | 46 | 45 | 57 | 59 | 49 | 57 | 64 | 48 |

## Student's answer

Stornoway is 58 degrees north in northern Scotland. Therefore it has a cold climate. This is shown by the low temperature of just 4 degrees in January and February. Summers are cold as well. What it does have is a lot of rainfall. Every month is wet. Again this is because of its location. Northern Scotland is one of the wettest parts of the UK. They get rain here when most other parts of Britain are dry. Low pressure and fronts bring a lot of rain from the Atlantic Ocean. I notice from the climate data that October is the month with most rain. One more thing about the temperature is that it ranges from 4 to 13.

## Examiner's verdict

Go through this answer and underline the places where the student is actually describing using the climate data for Stornoway. You won't find many! Then ask yourself what the description is worth – how many of the key characteristics, such as highest and lowest temperatures, temperature range, seasonal distribution of precipitation and some idea of the annual amount, have been mentioned? How significant is the specific data that has been included? Have the measurement units been stated? Notice that only part of the answer is description; much non-relevant explanation is included as well. The answer is also badly organised – what shows this?

**Overall**, a disappointing answer worth only 1 mark. It soon becomes clear that the student doesn't know what they are supposed to be looking for or what is significant. If you are in any doubt yourself, look at the Exam Preparation box on page 44 in your Understanding GCSE Geography textbook before trying to write a better answer.

## Do better

On the top of page 25 write an answer worth all 4 marks.

 **5 mins**

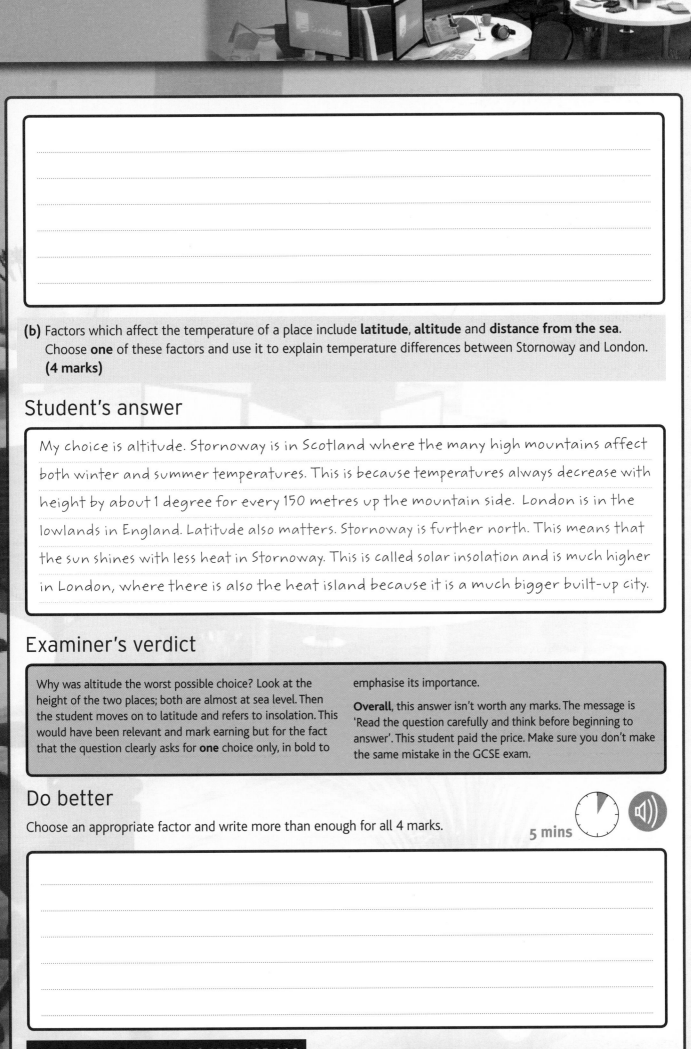

**(b)** Factors which affect the temperature of a place include **latitude**, **altitude** and **distance from the sea**. Choose **one** of these factors and use it to explain temperature differences between Stornoway and London. **(4 marks)**

## Student's answer

My choice is altitude. Stornoway is in Scotland where the many high mountains affect both winter and summer temperatures. This is because temperatures always decrease with height by about 1 degree for every 150 metres up the mountain side. London is in the lowlands in England. Latitude also matters. Stornoway is further north. This means that the sun shines with less heat in Stornoway. This is called solar insolation and is much higher in London, where there is also the heat island because it is a much bigger built-up city.

## Examiner's verdict

Why was altitude the worst possible choice? Look at the height of the two places; both are almost at sea level. Then the student moves on to latitude and refers to insolation. This would have been relevant and mark earning but for the fact that the question clearly asks for **one** choice only, in bold to emphasise its importance.

**Overall**, this answer isn't worth any marks. The message is 'Read the question carefully and think before beginning to answer'. This student paid the price. Make sure you don't make the same mistake in the GCSE exam.

## Do better

Choose an appropriate factor and write more than enough for all 4 marks.

5 mins

# Living World

## Summary

There is a great variety in natural ecosystems, both small scale such as hedgerows, and global such as tropical rainforest, hot desert and temperate deciduous forest. The natural balance between components (climate, soil, plants and animals) that make up ecosystems is being disturbed more and more by people. Tropical rainforests in particular are under threat from logging, mining, farming, road building and general population pressure. This increases the need for management to try to ensure future sustainability of natural ecosystems.

## Checklists for revision

| KEY IDEAS | Understand and know | Need more revision |
|---|---|---|
| **Ecosystems are made up of physical and human components which depend upon each other** | | |
| I know what an ecosystem is. | | |
| I can explain how an ecosystem works and know how the different parts are interrelated. | | |
| I can write about an example of a small-scale ecosystem. | | |
| **Temperate deciduous woodland is adapted to a cool wet climate; it provides examples of sustainable management** | | |
| I can describe the vegetation characteristics and explain how the vegetation is adapted to climate and soils. | | |
| I can name ways in which deciduous woodland is managed. | | |
| **Tropical rainforests are adapted to a hot wet climate; they are under threat and need to be managed sustainably** | | |
| I can describe and explain the forest structure in a tropical rainforest. | | |
| I can state three causes of rainforest removal and describe three impacts. | | |
| I can describe methods of management for conservation and future sustainability of rainforests. | | |

| CASE STUDIES – can you write about an area of each of these three types of vegetation referring to location, uses, challenges and management? | | |
|---|---|---|
| Hot desert | | |
| Deciduous forest | | |
| Tropical rainforest | | |

# Quick test

**10 mins**

Fill in the ecosystem boxes using the information given about climate, plants and their adaptations, soils and locations. (The number of pieces of information is the same for each ecosystem).

| Information | Global ecosystems | | |
| --- | --- | --- | --- |
| | Hot desert | Deciduous forest | Tropical rainforest |
| **1 Climate** (3 marks)<br>• hot and wet all year<br>• cool winter, warm summer<br>• hot and dry all year | | | |
| **summer** **winter** **annual rainfall**<br>17°C  4°C  about 750mm<br>35°C  20°C  under 250mm<br>27°C  27°C  over 2000mm | | | |
| **2 Plants** (3 marks)<br>• bluebells  • cactus<br>• lianas  • oak<br>  and epiphytes  • mahogany<br>• thorn scrub | | | |
| **3 Plant adaptations** (3 marks)<br>• broad fleshy leaves  • buttress roots<br>• leaves with drip tips  • succulent stems<br>• thorns not leaves  • winter leaf fall | | | |
| **4 Soils** (3 marks)<br>• 20–30 metres deep  • brown earth<br>• high pH (above 5)  • latosol<br>• loose sand/rock  • saline | | | |
| **5 Locations**<br>**(a) Latitude** (2 marks)<br>• 0–20°<br>• 20–30°<br>• 50–60°<br>**(b) Main continents** (2 marks)<br>• Africa, Asia and Latin America<br>• Europe, North America and Asia<br>• All except Europe<br>**(c) Countries** (4 marks)<br>• Brazil  • Egypt  • France<br>• Japan  • Malaysia  • Mexico<br>• Nigeria  • Pakistan  • UK | | | |

# Characteristics of vegetation in global ecosystems – label and complete

Add these labels to the diagrams where appropriate. Then answer the short questions.

| | | | | | |
|---|---|---|---|---|---|
| **Vegetation** | cactus | canopy | emergents | forest layers | layer of young trees and shrubs |
| | ground (herb) layer | lianas | succulent stems | thorns | thorn scrub under-canopy |
| **Roots** | branching | buttress | deep rooting system | | shallow surface |
| **Soils** | brown earth | latosol | organic humus layer | saline | sandy |

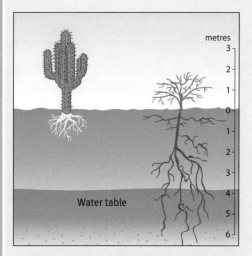

Water table

## Hot desert vegetation

**1** What is the water table?

.................................................................................

**2** What is the main problem for plant growth?

.................................................................................

**3** Why are the plants' roots so different?

.................................................................................

.................................................................................

.................................................................................

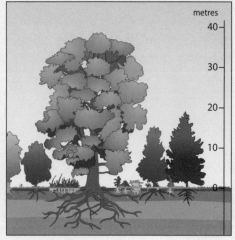

## Temperate deciduous forest

**4** What is a deciduous tree?

.................................................................................

.................................................................................

**5** Why are the trees deciduous?

.................................................................................

.................................................................................

.................................................................................

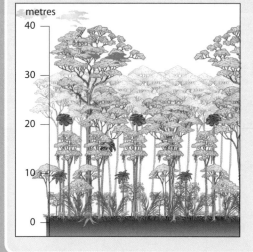

## Tropical rainforest

**6** What are the two big advantages for plant growth?

.................................................................................

.................................................................................

**7** What shows that this is a very competitive plant community?

.................................................................................

.................................................................................

.................................................................................

# How sustainable are human activities in tropical rainforests?

10 mins

### A Food and farming

1 Traditional ways of life – hunting and gathering, slash and burn farming

2 Commercial farming – cattle ranching, crop growing (e.g. soya beans, rice)

### B Mining and logging

1 Companies extracting minerals from surface pits and opencast mines

2 Logging companies clearing all trees and burning those they don't want

3 Selective logging – felling only trees with high commercial values

### C Settlement and infrastructure

1 Road building – straight routes through the forest, eventually paved

2 Settlement – towns grow as service centres for the workers

### D Tourism

1 Ecotourism – small lodges for visitor viewing of rainforest plants and animals

2 National Parks, nature reserves – large areas protected

1 Place each activity in the table below according to whether you consider it to be sustainable or unsustainable.

2 Then explain how and why each activity is sustainable or not. The first has been completed to show you what to do.

| | Human activity | How and why it is sustainable/unsustainable |
|---|---|---|
| Sustainable | A1 Traditional ways of life | Small numbers of people, low levels of technology, little impact on forest, any clearance soon reclaimed by forest |
| | | |
| Unsustainable | | |

## TEMPERATE DECIDUOUS WOODLAND

Location ...............................................................................

**Uses**

Uses of the timber ...............................................................

...............................................................................

...............................................................................

...............................................................................

Other uses of the forests ....................................................

...............................................................................

...............................................................................

...............................................................................

**Methods of sustainable management**

...............................................................................

...............................................................................

...............................................................................

...............................................................................

...............................................................................

## TROPICAL RAINFOREST

Location ...............................................................................

**Causes of deforestation**

Farming ...............................................................................

...............................................................................

Other causes ........................................................................

...............................................................................

**Impacts of deforestation**

Environmental .......................................................................

...............................................................................

Social ...............................................................................

...............................................................................

Other ...............................................................................

...............................................................................

**Methods of sustainable management**

...............................................................................

...............................................................................

...............................................................................

## HOT DESERT – rich area of the world

Location ...............................................................................

**Economic uses**

...............................................................................

...............................................................................

...............................................................................

...............................................................................

...............................................................................

...............................................................................

**Challenges faced**

...............................................................................

...............................................................................

...............................................................................

**Management for a sustainable future**

...............................................................................

...............................................................................

...............................................................................

## HOT DESERT – poor area of the world

Location ...............................................................................

**Economic uses**

...............................................................................

...............................................................................

...............................................................................

...............................................................................

...............................................................................

...............................................................................

**Challenges faced**

...............................................................................

...............................................................................

...............................................................................

**Management for a sustainable future**

...............................................................................

...............................................................................

...............................................................................

# EXAMINATION TECHNIQUE

10 mins

**1** Annotate (label) the soil profiles to show the characteristics of **(a)** tropical rainforest and **(b)** temperate deciduous forest soils. **(4 marks)**

**Before you start, read the 'Guide to labelling soil profiles' and 'Useful labels'.**

## Guide to labelling soil profiles

• name of soil
• horizons
• colour
• depth
• changes with depth

## Useful labels

horizon

brown earth

dark brown/black

organic layer

red/yellowish red

gradual change in colour from ............ to ............

sharp/no sharp boundary between horizons

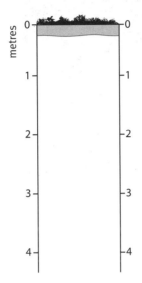

**(a)** Tropical rainforest

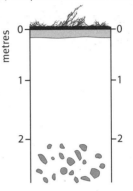

**(b)** Temperate deciduous forest

**2 (a)** Describe the main characteristics of the hot desert climate shown. **(4 marks)**

**(b)** Use the data to describe the main problem for vegetation growth in this climate. **(2 marks)**

## Guide to what to look for

**Temperature**

• highest monthly temp.
• lowest monthly temp.
• annual range (difference)
• adjectives (e.g. cold, hot)

**Rainfall**

• distribution (e.g. all year, wet season, dry season)
• annual total
• adjectives (e.g. wet, dry)

### Dubai – climate data

|                     | J  | F  | M  | A  | M  | J  | J  | A  | S  | O  | N  | D  |
|---------------------|----|----|----|----|----|----|----|----|----|----|----|----|
| Temperature (°C)    | 18 | 19 | 22 | 24 | 28 | 31 | 33 | 34 | 31 | 28 | 25 | 20 |
| Precipitation (mm)  | 23 | 23 | 10 | 5  | 0  | 0  | 0  | 0  | 0  | 0  | 0  | 10 |

**(a)** Describe the main characteristics of the hot desert climate shown. **(4 marks)**

......................................................................................................................................................

......................................................................................................................................................

......................................................................................................................................................

......................................................................................................................................................

......................................................................................................................................................

......................................................................................................................................................

**(b)** Use the data to describe the main problem for vegetation growth in this climate. **(2 marks)**

......................................................................................................................................................

......................................................................................................................................................

# GradeStudio

## GCSE EXAM QUESTIONS

### Question 1

Study the photograph taken in the tropical lowlands of Central America, in an area cleared of tropical rainforest.

**(a)** Give one piece of evidence from the photograph which suggests that the land was previously covered by forest. **(1 mark)**

**(b)** Is there a high risk of environmental damage in the area shown in the photograph? Use evidence from the photograph to help you explain your answer. **(4 marks)**

## Student's answer

(a) There are still plenty of trees at the back of the photo, and they look quite tall and dense. Trees like these must have grown in the field now used for cattle rearing. Also I can see logs and bits of wood in the field which might be remains from the old forest.

(b) Cattle are responsible for releasing greenhouse gases like methane. Methane is even worse for the atmosphere than carbon dioxide, because it stays there longer before breaking down and will remain a greenhouse gas trapping the Earth's heat for hundreds of years. It is also helping to make the ozone hole bigger. I agree with all those people who think that global warming is the world's greatest problem, causing rising sea levels and flooding coasts. Cutting down rainforests is bad for many other reasons. These are the largest and densest forests in the world which are just too valuable to lose.

## Examiner's verdict

To part (a) the answer is splendid. To part (b) it is a disaster. Why the difference? What did the student do in (a) that they didn't do in (b)? The answer in (a) was based on what could be seen in the photograph; also more than enough was written to make sure of the mark. In (b), apart from mention of cattle, there is no evidence of photograph use. Instead the student goes off at a tangent, all about global warming, showing lack of knowledge about human use of chemicals as the real cause of ozone depletion. It is often hard to understand why students take the wrong road like this in examinations. The main message is – read the question carefully before beginning to answer, and keep looking back at the question while answering.

**Overall** – 1/1 for part (a), but at best 1/4 for part (b). What would it have been better for the student to write about in (b)? Local environmental issues such as chances of increased soil erosion or habitat loss, as well as using evidence from the photograph to assess how high the risk might be.

## Do better

On the top of page 33 write an answer to question **1(b)** worth all 4 marks.

**4 mins**

## Question 2

Describe the challenges faced by people in hot desert areas and show how they are different between rich and poor parts of the world. Refer to suitable examples to illustrate your answer. **(8 marks)**

### Student's answer

An example of a hot desert in a rich part of the world is the desert west of the USA. The desert states are Arizona, Utah, Colorado and New Mexico. All these states are sparsely populated. Mining for minerals such as copper, uranium and coal, and farming growing fruit and vegetables and keeping cattle are the main economic activities. The main problem for farmers is obtaining enough irrigation water. This is why many big dams have been built along the Colorado and other rivers, like the Hoover Dam, where water is stored in Lake Mead so that there is an all year round water supply to make use of the plentiful desert sunshine. Another economic activity which is growing is tourism. Las Vegas with its big glitzy hotels and casinos is the centre of the tourist industry. More and more visitors are making worse the problem of water supply.

An example of a hot desert in a poor part of the world is the Thar desert in the south of Pakistan. Farming is the main activity here. Keeping animals is more important than crop growing. Farmers keep a mixture of sheep, cattle, goats and camels. Because there is little good grass and water, the farmers need to be nomadic. Here they are just poor subsistence not rich commercial farmers as in the USA. There are no big dams in southern Pakistan

### Examiner's verdict

Are the two examples used suitable? Yes. Does the student have good case study knowledge? Yes. Has the student made best use of this knowledge to answer the question set? No. Is the focus of the answer on the question theme of challenges? No. Has the student begun with general challenges faced by people living in hot desert areas? No. Has student explained why they are different between the two examples? Not really, perhaps with the exception of the last two lines.

**Overall**, only Level 1, worth 3 or 4 marks. Grade D standard. Skirting around the question set meant that the student did not gain full reward for their case study knowledge.

### Do better

Write an answer worthy of 8 marks on a separate piece of lined paper.

10 mins

HOW WELL DID YOU DO? SEE PAGES 116–7

# Water on the Land

## Summary

Water on the land is about rivers and their work. Rivers erode land surfaces in the uplands, transport loose materials downstream and deposit silt in the lowlands. They form V-shaped valleys and other distinctive landforms. When rivers flood, they cause devastation and destruction. People respond using hard and soft methods of flood protection. However, rivers are also vital sources of water supply, which is another reason why people are interested in managing rivers.

## Checklist for revision

| KEY IDEAS | Understand and know | Need more revision |
|---|---|---|
| **The shape of river valleys and the dominant river processes change downstream** | | |
| I can name three different ways a river and its valley change from source to mouth. | | |
| I know four processes of erosion and can name four processes of transportation. | | |
| I know the long profile of a river and how the valley cross-section changes downstream. | | |
| **Distinctive landforms result as rivers flow downstream** | | |
| I can explain how waterfalls and gorges are formed by river erosion. | | |
| I know why rivers form meanders and ox-bow lakes in their lower courses. | | |
| I can name two landforms produced by river flooding and explain how they are formed. | | |
| **The amount of water in rivers fluctuates; rivers flood due to a number of physical and human causes** | | |
| I understand why some rivers are described as flashy, while others are slow to flood. | | |
| I can name three physical and two human causes of river floods. | | |
| **There is much debate about costs and benefits of strategies used to prevent flooding** | | |
| I know the difference between hard and soft engineering strategies for flood control. | | |
| I can give some of the costs and benefits of different strategies used to deal with river floods. | | |
| **The management of rivers to provide water supply raises issues** | | |
| I can explain why long-distance water-transfers from west to east are needed in the UK. | | |

| CASE STUDIES – can you name an example of each and write about it? | | |
|---|---|---|
| **River flooding in a rich part of the world** – causes, effects and responses | | |
| **River flooding in a poor part of the world** – causes, effects and responses | | |
| **A dam/reservoir in the UK** – advantages of its location, economic, social, environmental and sustainable supply issues | | |

# Quick test

**1 (a)** Name the **four** processes of river erosion **(clue: HASA)**.

........................................................................    ........................................................................

........................................................................    ........................................................................

**(4 marks)**

**(b)** Name the **four** processes of river transportation **(clue: TSSS)**.

........................................................................    ........................................................................

........................................................................    ........................................................................

**(4 marks)**

**2** Which of these favour **river deposition**? Cross out the wrong answer in each pair.

| | | |
|---|---|---|
| gentle / steep gradient | fast / slow river flow | inside / outside river bend |
| | large / small variations in river discharge between seasons | |

**(4 marks)**

**3** Which of these are more likely to cause river floods? Cross out the wrong answer in each pair.

| | |
|---|---|
| light rain / thunderstorm | ice freezing / snow melt |
| gentle slopes / steep relief | deforestation / reafforestation |
| farm land used for pasture / urban land uses | permeable rock / impermeable rocks |

**(6 marks)**

**4** Circle the odd one out and give a reason.

**(a)**     gorge          levée          steep V-shaped valley          waterfall

**Reason:** ........................................................................

........................................................................

........................................................................

**(b)**     dam       flood plain zoning       river straightening       walled river banks

**Reason:** ........................................................................

........................................................................

........................................................................

**(2 marks)**

# River landforms – shade, label and draw

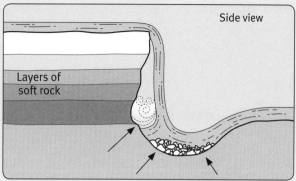

Side view

Layers of
soft rock

Front view

Waterfall slowly
retreating upstream

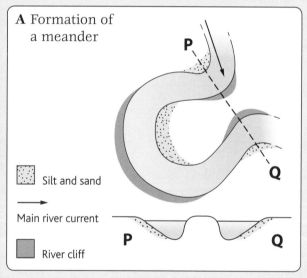

**Key**

☐ Hard rock layer          ☐ Impermeable rocks

## Upper course – waterfall and gorge

1  On both diagrams, shade in the hard rock layers and layers of impermeable rocks. Complete the key.

2  On the side view, write in suitable labels for the three arrows.

3  On the front view, mark O for the original position of the waterfall and label the gorge.

4  What will happen in future years and why?

.............................................................................

.............................................................................

.............................................................................

.............................................................................

.............................................................................

.............................................................................

.............................................................................

.............................................................................

## Lower course – meander and ox-bow lake

**A** Formation of a meander

P

Q

☐ Silt and sand

→ Main river current

■ River cliff

P          Q

**B**

5  Add labels to the diagrams in box A to show the features and formation of a meander.

6  In box B, draw another labelled diagram to show and explain how the meander might have become an ox-bow lake.

7  Why is this most likely to happen when the river is in flood? Try to state two reasons.

.......................................................................................................................

.......................................................................................................................

.......................................................................................................................

.......................................................................................................................

**5**

# Strategies for river management

**1** Eight strategies are illustrated in the sketches below. In the space below each one, name the strategy and state how it works.

**Hard engineering**

Name ..........................................

How it works ..........................................

..........................................

..........................................

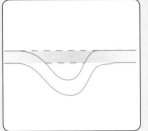

Name ..........................................

How it works ..........................................

..........................................

..........................................

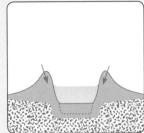

Name ..........................................

How it works ..........................................

..........................................

..........................................

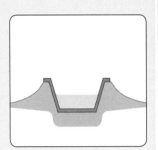

Name ..........................................

How it works ..........................................

..........................................

..........................................

**Soft engineering**

Name ..........................................

How it works ..........................................

..........................................

..........................................

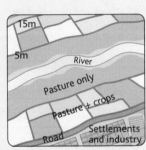

Name ..........................................

How it works ..........................................

..........................................

..........................................

Name ..........................................

How it works ..........................................

..........................................

..........................................

Name ..........................................

How it works ..........................................

..........................................

..........................................

**2** Choose one example of hard and soft engineering and fill in the boxes below.

| Hard engineering | Soft engineering |
|---|---|
| Strategy ........................ | Strategy ........................ |
| Advantages ........................ | Advantages ........................ |
| When/where is it the most suitable option? | When/where is it the most suitable option? |
| | |
| Disadvantages ........................ | Disadvantages ........................ |
| When/where is it a less suitable option? | When/where is it a less suitable option? |
| | |
| Likely people in favour or against its use? | Likely people in favour or against its use? |
| In favour ........................ | In favour ........................ |
| Against ........................ | Against ........................ |

**RIVER FLOODING –
in a poor part of the world**

Name of country .................................................

Location/places affected .................................................

.................................................

**Causes**

Physical .................................................

.................................................

.................................................

Human .................................................

**Effects**

.................................................

.................................................

.................................................

**People's responses**

Immediate/short-term .................................................

.................................................

Long-term impacts/prospects .................................................

.................................................

**RIVER FLOODING –
in a rich part of the world**

Name of country .................................................

Location/places affected .................................................

.................................................

**Causes**

Physical .................................................

.................................................

.................................................

Human .................................................

**Effects**

.................................................

.................................................

.................................................

**People's responses**

Immediate/short-term .................................................

.................................................

Long-term impacts/prospects .................................................

.................................................

**DAM/RESERVOIR in the UK**

Location .................................................

Advantages .................................................

.................................................

Water transfers/consumption .................................................

.................................................

**Issues resulting from its construction**

Economic .................................................

.................................................

Social .................................................

.................................................

Environmental .................................................

.................................................

Sustainable water supply .................................................

.................................................

**Overall – are benefits greater than costs?**

.................................................

.................................................

**EXAMPLE OF A UK RIVER**

e.g. the River Tees (pp. 83, 93 and 97 in textbook)

**Upper course landforms** – named examples

Gorge .................................................

Waterfall .................................................

**Profiles**

River long profile .................................................

Valley cross profile .................................................

**Human management**

.................................................

**Lower course landforms**

.................................................

.................................................

**Human management**

.................................................

.................................................

**Overall – do hard or soft strategies dominate?**

.................................................

## EXAMINATION TECHNIQUE

10 mins

**1** Explain how rivers form steep sided V-shaped valleys in the uplands. **(4 marks)**

**Arrange these five explanatory statements in the most logical order for a full mark GCSE answer.**

> As the valley becomes deeper, more rock and soil falls down the valley sides keeping them steep.
>
> This makes the valley deepest in the centre and V-shaped.
>
> Erosion is concentrated in the centre of the valley where the river is flowing.
>
> The river is flowing high above sea level and concentrates on cutting downwards.
>
> The river erodes downwards by processes such as abrasion and hydraulic action.

.................................................................................................................................

.................................................................................................................................

.................................................................................................................................

.................................................................................................................................

.............................................................................................................. **(4 marks)**

**2** Explain the formation of meanders and ox-bow lakes. **(5 marks)**

**Look at this GCSE answer. The student became very muddled. Cross out and correct the mistakes to make the answer worth the full 5 marks.**

> River meanders are formed by sideways erosion known as vertical erosion. When a
>
> river flows around a bend, the main river current swings against the inside bend
>
> where erosion takes place, leading to the formation of a slip-off slope. At the outside
>
> bend on the other side of the channel, river flow is weak; here the river deposits
>
> some of its load forming a gentle river cliff. Over time, continued vertical erosion
>
> on two outside bends leads to a narrower meander scar being formed. In times of
>
> flood, erosion by the river's hydraulic action cuts through the two inside bends of the
>
> meander so that the river flows straight, leaving a small round lake known as an
>
> ox-bow lake.

## PRACTICE GCSE QUESTIONS

Before looking at the answers from the student and comments from the examiner, make a careful study of the photograph. Think about the answers that you would have given to this GCSE exam question.

### Question 1

Study the photograph of a river in the Alps of Germany.

**(a) (i)** Which part of the river's course is shown?

**(1 mark)**

**(ii)** Describe how the evidence from the photograph supports your answer. **(4 marks)**

**(b)** The discharge of the river shown in the photograph varies greatly during the year. Suggest reasons why this river sometimes carries a much greater amount of water. **(4 marks)**

Read the student's answers. Cover up the Examiner's verdict. How many marks do you think each answer is worth?

**(a)(i)** Which part of the river's course is shown? **(1 mark)**

### Student's answer

> It has to be its upper course.

**(ii)** Describe how the evidence from the photograph supports your answer. **(4 marks)**

### Student's answer

> In upper courses rivers are flowing through mountains and hills.
> They are flowing well above sea level, meaning that they are cutting down
> to reach sea level. This is known as vertical erosion. Typical landforms
> which you will find in the upper course of all rivers are V- shaped valleys
> that are steep sided, interlocking spurs, waterfalls and gorges. You would
> expect the river to be flowing fast because of the steep gradient and its easy
> flow over its rocky bed.

**(b)** The discharge of the river shown in the photograph varies greatly during the year. Suggest reasons why this river sometimes carries a much greater amount of water. **(4 marks)**

## Student's answer

This river is an Alpine river. Coming from the mountains means that rainfall and snowfall will be heavy and high. There are many glaciers in the high parts of the Alps. In summer this river like all the other Alpine rivers will be full of water. It will be much deeper and much more fast flowing than it is now. This is because the ice and snow melts. If there is heavy rain in summer as well, then this will cause very big river floods. All the Alpine rivers do this and it is this which makes them so good for generating HEP.

Now read what the examiner had to say about these answers.

## Examiner's verdict

1(a)(i) Upper course is a correct start – 1 mark.

(ii) Only 1, or at best, 2 marks. The main problem is that the student has made so little use of what can be observed in the photograph. Making observations from the photograph is absolutely essential to obey the command word 'Describe'. Most of the answer is about the typical features of the upper course of all rivers, not just this river – good knowledge, but has it been used and applied to this river? At most this candidate has taken 'mountains', 'river flowing fast' and 'rocky bed' from the photograph.

(b) This answer is worth only 2 marks. Only one reason has been used for explaining greater amounts of river water. This is amount and type of rainfall. In a question asking for reasons and worth four marks, reference to just one reason is not enough. There is another problem – not making sufficient use of the photograph, again. Why did the candidate not take note of other features affecting river discharge that can be seen on the photograph?

**Overall** – worth 4 or 5 of the 9 marks, barely a Grade C performance. The candidate's knowledge about the upper course was probably strong enough for a better answer, but they were let down by a failure in technique – not giving answers that best fitted the questions set.

## Do better

Write full mark answers to 1(a)(ii) **(4 marks)** and (b) **(4 marks).**

10 mins

(a)(ii) ..........................................................................................................................................................................
..............................................................................................................................................................................
..............................................................................................................................................................................
..............................................................................................................................................................................
..............................................................................................................................................................................
..............................................................................................................................................................................
..............................................................................................................................................................................
.......................................................................................................................................................... **(4 marks)**

(b) ...........................................................................................................................................................................
..............................................................................................................................................................................
..............................................................................................................................................................................
..............................................................................................................................................................................
..............................................................................................................................................................................
..............................................................................................................................................................................
.......................................................................................................................................................... **(4 marks)**

HOW WELL DID YOU DO? SEE PAGE 117

# Ice on the Land

## Summary

In the last Ice Age, snow, ice and glaciers covered most of the British Isles. Today, there are no glaciers in the British Isles but where glaciers still exist, such as in polar regions and in high mountains, they are retreating. Ice is a powerful agent of erosion, making big changes to landscapes it passes over. Left behind are many distinctive landforms. In the mountains, landforms of erosion dominate; in the lowlands, there are landforms of transportation and deposition. Snow-covered mountains attract tourists, but many ski resorts are worried by retreating glaciers.

## Checklists for revision

| KEY IDEAS | Understand and know | Need more revision |
|---|---|---|
| **The amount of ice on the Earth's surface keeps changing; the amount of ice depends on the glacial budget** | | |
| I understand why glaciers keep advancing and retreating. | | |
| I know the differences between an ice sheet and a valley glacier. | | |
| **Ice is a powerful force shaping the land; weathering, erosion, transportation and deposition all contribute** | | |
| I can explain how freeze–thaw weathering operates. | | |
| I can name two processes of glacial erosion and explain how they erode the land. | | |
| I know when, where and why glaciers deposit their loads. | | |
| **Distinctive landforms result from these different processes** | | |
| I understand the formation of a corrie. | | |
| I can describe the main features of glaciated valleys. | | |
| I know how glacial troughs are formed. | | |
| I can name four landforms of glacial deposition and can describe differences in their appearance and location. | | |
| **Snow and ice landscapes attract tourists, but this leads to conflicts and issues over use of such areas** | | |
| I can list the attractions of the Alps for winter sports and their impacts (both good and bad). | | |
| **Glacial retreat poses a threat to the economies of areas relying on tourism** | | |
| I can explain the problems for tourism caused by too little snowfall. | | |

| CASE STUDIES – can you name an example of each and write about it? | | |
|---|---|---|
| **A glacier** – location, evidence for advance and retreat, reasons for these shifts | | |
| **Alpine area for winter sports** – location, attractions for tourists, impacts of tourists, management and issues for the future | | |

# Quick test – top twenty glacial terms

**10 mins**

1 Choose from the top twenty glacial terms in the box to complete **(a)** to **(l)**.
You will use each term once.

| | | | | | |
|---|---|---|---|---|---|
| ablation | abrasion | accumulation | arête | boulder clay | bulldozing |
| corrie | drumlin | freeze–thaw | glacial trough | ground | lateral |
| medial | plucking | pyramidal | ribbon | rotational slip | tarn | terminal | U-shape |

**(a) Two** terms to explain the glacial budget of ice advance and retreat

.......................................................................................................................

**(b) Two** processes of glacial erosion

.......................................................................................................................

**(c) One** type of weathering common in cold regions

.......................................................................................................................

**(d) One** process of movement inside a corrie

.......................................................................................................................

**(e) Two** words which describe the shape and appearance of mountain peaks

.......................................................................................................................

**(f) Two** terms which refer to glaciated valleys

.......................................................................................................................

**(g) Four** types of moraine

.......................................................................................................................

**(h) Two** examples of glacial lakes

.......................................................................................................................

**(i) One** name for the movement of a glacier pushing forward the ice front

.......................................................................................................................

**(j) One** name for the unsorted materials deposited by glaciers

.......................................................................................................................

**(k) One** feature which forms 'basket of eggs' topography

.......................................................................................................................

**(l) One** name for the hollow high on a mountainside where valley glaciers begin

.......................................................................................................................

**(20 marks)**

2 **(a)** Give the differences between ice sheets and valley glaciers.

Size ...................................................................................................................

Location ............................................................................................................

**(3 marks)**

**(b)** Give the differences between the Pleistocene period and today.

.......................................................................................... **(2 marks)**

# Glacial landforms – shade and label

## Snow and ice covered mountains

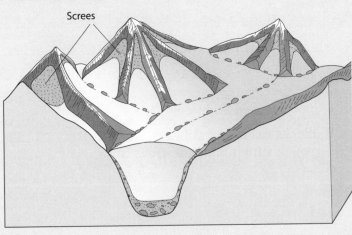

Screes

**1 (a)** On the sketch

    **(i)** shade areas covered by snow and ice

    **(ii)** label **two** types of mountain peak and **three** types of moraine.

    **(b)(i)** Name the process which forms the scree.

        **(ii)** Where is the scree forming in this area?

        **(iii)** Why is it forming here?

## Glacial trough and mountains after the ice has melted

**2** On the sketch

    **(a)** shade in the floor and sides of the glacial trough

    **(b)** label the different types of mountain peaks and lakes

    **(c)** label **four** hanging valleys 'H' and **five** truncated spurs 'T'

    **(d)** add other labels to describe the characteristics of the glacial trough.

## Glacial deposition in the lowlands

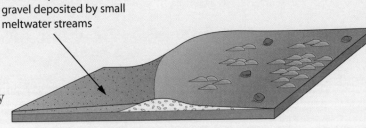

Outwash plain of sand and gravel deposited by small meltwater streams

**3 (a)** On the sketch

    **(i)** shade in the area previously covered by a glacier

    **(ii)** label terminal moraine, drumlins, basket of eggs topography, erratic rocks and boulder clay.

    **(b)** Describe the main characteristics of boulder clay.

    **(c)** How and why are outwash plain deposits, formed by small meltwater streams, different to boulder clay?

# Tourism threats in Alpine areas

## The avalanche hazard

The box below contains information about avalanches.

A  deforestation or trees dying from acid rain reduces slope stability

B  blocks roads and railways, cuts off power supplies and destroys trees

C  vibrations trigged off by skiers or traffic

D  avalanche shed over the tops of roads and railways to protect them

E  trained rescue services equipped with dogs and helicopters

F  half of deaths among skiers (most of them while skiing off-piste)

G  snow fences and V-shaped avalanche breakers to divert snow in safe places

H  average speed of 40–60 km per hour

I  early warning systems to predict times when risk is likely to be high

J  kills people (average of over 100 deaths per year in the Alps)

K  reafforestation can reduce damage by 50 per cent

L  steep slopes where snow and ice cover is less stable

M  heavy snowfalls add to weight of earlier snowfalls and become less stable

N  sudden increase in temperature due to sunshine or warm winds

O  sudden downhill movement of snow, ice and/or rock

**1**  Arrange the information about avalanches under the correct headings. Indicate your choice by writing the capital letter that accompanies the statement next to one of the following.

**(a) Definition** ............................  ............................

**(b) Causes** ............................  ............................  ............................  ............................

**(c) Effects** ............................  ............................  ............................

**(d) Management strategies** ............................  ............................  ............................  ............................  ............................

## Environmental impacts from Alpine tourism growth

**2**  Fill in the boxes with details of environmental damage likely to result.

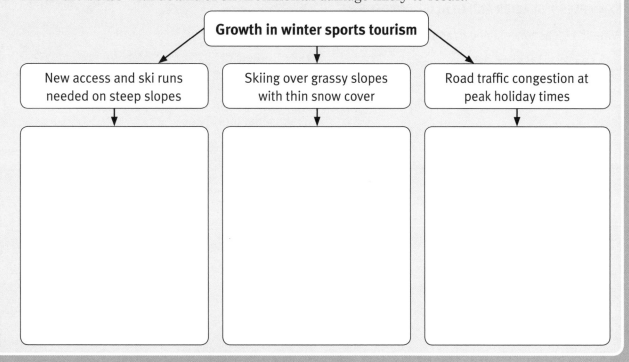

## A GLACIER

Name ..................................................................

Location ..............................................................

**Features and appearance** ...................................

..................................................................

..................................................................

..................................................................

..................................................................

..................................................................

..................................................................

**Retreat since 19th century**

Evidence .............................................................

..................................................................

..................................................................

..................................................................

..................................................................

**Causes**

..................................................................

..................................................................

..................................................................

..................................................................

## ALPINE AREA FOR WINTER SPORTS

Name of area ........................................................

Location ..............................................................

**Attractions for tourists**

..................................................................

..................................................................

**Impacts of tourists**

Economic .............................................................

..................................................................

Social .................................................................

..................................................................

Environmental ......................................................

..................................................................

**Management strategies**

..................................................................

..................................................................

..................................................................

Level of success ....................................................

..................................................................

..................................................................

## EXAMPLES – GLACIER AND GLACIAL LANDFORMS

Write in at least one named example of each feature.

Ice sheet ...................................

Valley glacier ...................................

Arête ...................................

Pyramidal (horn) peak ...................................

Corrie ...................................

Tarn lake ...................................

U-shaped valley ...................................

Ribbon lake ...................................

Hanging valley ...................................

Scree slope ...................................

Terminal moraine ...................................

Drumlins ...................................

# EXAMINATION TECHNIQUE

**1(a)** Describe the physical features of a corrie. **(4 marks)**

**(b)** Explain the formation of a corrie and tarn lake. **(6 marks)**

**All the statements needed for full mark exam answers to questions (a) and (b) are written below. Choose the statements needed for each answer; then write them out in a good order for full mark GCSE answers.**

> Water from daytime melting runs down the steep back wall.
>
> Open at the front with a rock lip.
>
> Melting water seeps into the bergschrund crevasse leading to freeze–thaw on the headwall.
>
> Snow and ice accumulate and grow into small glaciers below mountain tops.
>
> Freeze–thaw provides pieces of rock used as tools for abrasion.
>
> High on a mountain side.
>
> A rock lip forms near the end of the hollow due to less powerful erosion.
>
> Steep rocky backwall.
>
> Water accumulates in the hollow with the rock lip as a dam.
>
> As the glacier moves, the hollow is made deeper by abrasion and plucking.
>
> Circular hollow.
>
> A small circular lake often fills the corrie hollow.
>
> Due to rotational slip, greater ice pressure erodes the back of the hollow more than the front.
>
> Rock walls on three sides leading to arête peaks above.

**(a)** Describe the physical features of a corrie.

.......................................................................................................................................
.......................................................................................................................................
.......................................................................................................................................
.......................................................................................................................................
.......................................................................................................................................
....................................................................................................... **(4 marks)**

**(b)** Explain the formation of a corrie and tarn lake.

.......................................................................................................................................
.......................................................................................................................................
.......................................................................................................................................
.......................................................................................................................................
.......................................................................................................................................
.......................................................................................................................................
....................................................................................................... **(6 marks)**

Why is a good order vital when explaining landform formation?

.......................................................................................................................................

# PRACTICE GCSE QUESTIONS

## Question 1

Study the photograph which shows a valley glacier in the Swiss Alps. Annotate (label) the physical features shown on the photograph. **(4 marks)**

Valley Glacier

mountain peaks arêtes and some pyramidal

corrie hollows below

steep rocky valley sides

many ice crevasses

long lines of medial moraine

I think the glacier is starting to deposit moraine because it is melting.

## Examiner's verdict

Oh dear! This candidate just doesn't understand how to annotate or label a photograph. There is nothing wrong with writing labels in the empty spaces around the photo provided that lines or arrows then link labels to the features themselves on the photo. Even so, for some features it may be better to annotate or label on the photograph itself. Valley glacier is no use for a heading when it is stated in the question. The sentence below about the glacier melting and starting to deposit is irrelevant because this is explanation not description.

What of the physical features identified by the candidate?

Can they be seen on the photo – is the geography correct? Basically the answer is yes; the candidate's glaciation knowledge seems good enough. What the candidate has failed to do is to link the written labels to their locations.

**Overall** – This answer might be given 0 marks. No annotation, no labels on the photograph, no indication of locations. Therefore no marks. Wouldn't this be a disastrous outcome for a candidate with geographical knowledge, who had obviously looked at the photograph?

## Do better

Accurately label the features on the photograph to gain all 4 marks. You could amend and add to the student's answer and draw linking lines to link the features to the features themselves in the photo, or you could start from scratch.

**4 mins**

## Question 2

Using a case study of an Alpine area which attracts many tourists, explain the impacts on the environment that result and describe how they can be reduced. **(8 marks)**

### Student's answer

Switzerland and Austria are examples of Alpine areas that attract many tourists. Many skiers visit in winter, but others go in summer to see the beautiful scenery of snow capped mountains and large blue lakes. Examples of places visited by lots of tourists include Zermatt to see the Matterhorn and Lake Garda in the Italian Lake District. The trouble is that these visitors cause many problems.[1]

The high parts of the Alps are known as a fragile environment, because vegetation struggles to survive here during the very cold winters. The last thing the grass needs is for visitors to try to ski on it when the snow is not deep enough. Many skiers come in their cars; roads are choked with traffic in the holiday season, making the problem of acid rain worse. This is killing off more trees. Lots of trees have already been cleared for building the ski runs. Because slopes are steep, the risks of soil erosion and avalanches are now greater than ever.[2]

Good management is needed to reduce all these problems.[3]

### Examiner's verdict

Good in parts!

**1 First paragraph**
Is it full of relevant case study information? Unfortunately, no. It refers to Alpine areas but without making the content relevant to this question. It is merely general information about Alpine tourism.

**2 Second paragraph**
Is it full of relevant content about impacts on the

environment of visitors to Alpine areas? Yes it is. A range of points is included. This is the mark-earning part.

**3 Third paragraph**
The one sentence about reducing the problems merely highlights that the candidate does not try to answer the second part of the question.

**Overall**, top of Level 1 or bottom of Level 2, just about Grade C standard, for what is a part-answer to the question.

### Do better

Impacts on the environment have been adequately covered. On a separate piece of lined paper, spend 5 or 6 minutes adding what is needed to change this from a 4 mark to an 8 mark answer. Describe how impacts can be reduced and incorporate some real case study information that matches the question set.

5 mins

HOW WELL DID YOU DO? SEE PAGE 117

# The Coastal Zone

## Summary

The coastal zone focuses on the area between the high and low water marks, an area under constant change. Along some stretches of coast, cliffs collapse and coastal erosion is rapid. Various management strategies are in place, some hard and some soft, but losses of land continue, leading to discussion about how the coast should be managed. In contrast, along other stretches of coast, waves deposit sand and shingle, adding to the coastline by forming landforms of deposition.

## Checklists for revision

| KEY IDEAS | Understand and know | Need more revision |
|---|---|---|
| **The coast is shaped by weathering, mass movement, erosion, transportation and deposition** | | |
| I know the differences between weathering, mass movement and wave erosion. | | |
| I can state and explain the differences between destructive and constructive waves. | | |
| I can name four processes of wave erosion. | | |
| I can describe how sand and shingle are transported along the coast in the UK. | | |
| **Different landforms result from the processes of erosion and deposition** | | |
| I can recognise and name at least five landforms of coastal erosion. | | |
| I know where and why beaches form. | | |
| I can describe what a spit looks like and explain why it forms. | | |
| **Cliff collapse causes major problems** | | |
| I can give at least two reasons why some cliffs are being eroded fast. | | |
| **There is much debate about how the coast should be managed** | | |
| I can give examples of hard and soft methods of engineering for coastal protection and can state differences between them. | | |
| I can give the advantages and disadvantages of different methods of coastal management. | | |
| **There is a need for conservation to protect unique coastal environments** | | |
| I know what is meant by 'managed retreat' of the coastline and can explain why this leads to conflicts with other land uses. | | |

| CASE STUDIES – can you name an example of each and write about it? | | |
|---|---|---|
| **Cliff collapse** – causes and impacts on people | | |
| **Coastal flooding** – causes and economic, social, political, and environmental impacts | | |
| **Coastal management** – why needed, methods used, costs and benefits | | |
| **Coastal habitat** – its natural environment and strategies for conservation and sustainable uses | | |

## Quick test

**6 mins**

Circle the correct answer to each of these questions.

**1** Identify the type of wave which erodes cliffs.

    constructive                        destructive                  swash

**2** Identify the process which loosens and breaks off bits of rock at the top of cliffs and on cliff faces.

    erosion                            mass movement          weathering

**3** Landslides and slumping which help to cause cliff collapse are examples of what?

    erosion                            mass movement          hydraulic action

**4** What is the process of wave erosion caused by the impact of sea water against cliff faces called?

    abrasion                         attrition                 weathering

**5** What is the transport of sand and pebbles along the coast by waves called?

    constructive waves          longshore drift          suspension

**6** Building sea walls and flood barriers are examples of what?

    hard engineering          managed retreat          soft engineering

**7** What is doing nothing to protect the coastline and allowing the sea to invade the land called?

    hard engineering          managed retreat          soft engineering

**(7 marks)**

## Odd one out

**4 mins**

Circle the odd one out and give a reason.

**1**   beach                          cave                        cliff

    **Reason:** ......................................................................................................

.............................................................................................................................

**2**   bar                           beach                   spit

    **Reason:** ......................................................................................................

.............................................................................................................................

**3**   groynes                    marsh creation          sand dune regeneration

    **Reason:** ......................................................................................................

.............................................................................................................................

**(3 marks)**

# Coastal landforms – shade and label

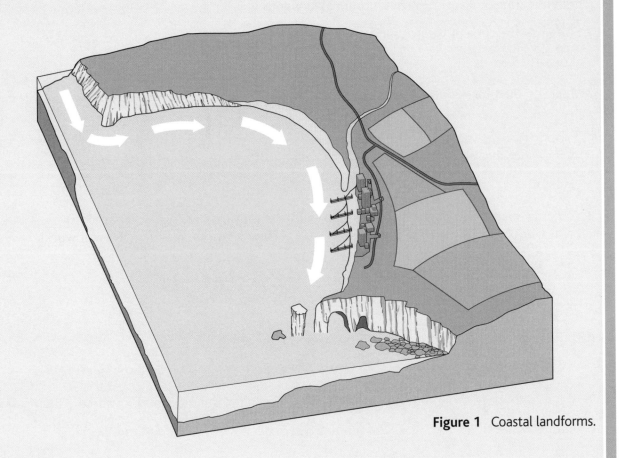

**Figure 1** Coastal landforms.

On the sketch above

1  Shade in and label **(a)** the cliffs and **(b)** the beach.

2  Add the labels in the box below to the diagram where appropriate.

| arch | bay | cave | headland | spit | stack | wave-cut platform |
|------|-----|------|----------|------|-------|-------------------|

3  **(a)** What is the evidence for coastal management by people along one part of this coast?

   ......................................................................................................................................

   **(b)** Why was it done? ..............................................................................................

4  There are three pieces of evidence for the movement of the longshore drift from top to bottom in **Figure 1**. Can you list all three of them?

   **(a)** ...............................................................................................................................

   **(b)** ...............................................................................................................................

   **(c)** ...............................................................................................................................

5  HAAS is a memory aid (mnemonic) for processes of wave erosion.

   Name the four processes in the spaces below. Always refer to them when explaining the formation of coastal landforms of erosion.

   H ................................................    A ................................................

   A ................................................    S ................................................

# Strategies for coastal management

1 Seven strategies are illustrated in the sketches below. In the space below each one,
   **(i)** name the strategy and **(ii)** state how it works.

## Hard engineering

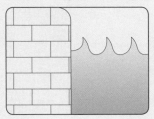  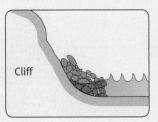  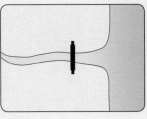  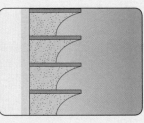

Name ......................

Name ......................

Name ......................

Name ......................

How it works

How it works

How it works

How it works

## Soft engineering

  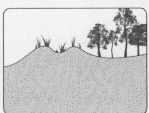  

Name ......................

Name ......................

Name ......................

How it works

How it works

How it works

2 Choose one example of hard and soft engineering and fill in the boxes below.

| **Hard engineering** | **Soft engineering** |
|---|---|
| Strategy ...................... | Strategy ...................... |
| Benefits ...................... | Benefits ...................... |
| Costs ...................... | Costs ...................... |
| People in favour ...................... | People in favour ...................... |
| Reasons why ...................... | Reasons why ...................... |
| For where is it suitable? | For where is it suitable? |
| People against ...................... | People against ...................... |
| Reasons why ...................... | Reasons why ...................... |
| For where is it unsuitable? | For where is it unsuitable? |
| Named example | Named example |

**Recent/threatened CLIFF COLLAPSE**

Name of area.............................................

Rate of coastal erosion ...............................

**Causes**

Physical ....................................................

........................................................................

........................................................................

Human......................................................

**Impacts**

On people's lives .......................................

........................................................................

On the environment ..................................

........................................................................

**People's responses**

........................................................................

........................................................................

Long term impacts/prospects....................

........................................................................

**COASTAL FLOODING**

Name of area.............................................

Location ....................................................

**Causes**

Why the risk of coastal flooding is high

........................................................................

........................................................................

........................................................................

**Impacts**

Economic ..................................................

........................................................................

Social .......................................................

........................................................................

........................................................................

Political ....................................................

........................................................................

Environmental..........................................

........................................................................

**COASTAL MANAGEMENT**

Location ....................................................

Reasons why needed .................................

**Methods used (strategies adopted)**

........................................................................

........................................................................

........................................................................

Hard or soft engineering? .........................

........................................................................

**Benefits** .................................................

........................................................................

**Costs** .....................................................

........................................................................

**Overall – are benefits greater than costs?**

........................................................................

........................................................................

........................................................................

**COASTAL HABITAT**

Location ....................................................

**Environmental characteristics** ..............

........................................................................

........................................................................

........................................................................

**Habitat/species living there** ................

........................................................................

........................................................................

Reasons why species inhabit it .................

........................................................................

**Strategies for conserving the environment**

........................................................................

........................................................................

........................................................................

How **sustainable** are the strategies?

........................................................................

........................................................................

# EXAMINATION TECHNIQUE

**10 mins**

**1** Explain the formation of sea cliffs. **(5 marks)**

**For a full mark answer, arrange these explanatory statements in the most logical order.**

Waves erode and undercut the rock face by processes such as abrasion and hydraulic action.

The rock above the notch is left overhanging.

This forms a wave-cut notch.

Eventually it collapses and the cliff face retreats inland.

As the overhang increases in size the weight of overhanging rock increases.

Destructive waves attack the bottom of a rock.

**(5 marks)**

**2 (a)** Describe the main features of spits. **(4 marks)**

  **(b)** Explain their formation. **(4 marks)**

**Identify and circle the five statements from the list below that describe the main features of spits and would give a full mark answer to 2(a).**

Sediments accumulate and extend the spit into the open sea.

Long narrow ridges of sand or shingle.

Eroded materials are carried along the coast by the longshore drift.

May be several kilometres long.

Like a beach that extends into the open sea.

The sea end of the spit may be curved into a hook by strong winds and currents.

Deposition begins at a bend in the coastline.

One end is attached to land the other is in the open sea.

Some are straight (e.g. Spurn Point) and others are hooked (e.g. Hurst Castle).

Constructive waves deposit sand and shingle away from the coast in the open sea.

**Arrange the remaining five statements to gain a full mark answer to 2(b).**

**(4 marks)**

# GradeStudio

## PRACTICE GCSE QUESTIONS

### Question 1

Study Photograph A. Describe the physical features shown in the photograph. **(4 marks)**

**Photograph A** Part of the Yorkshire coastline north of Flamborough Head

## Student's answer

I can see that the coast is being eroded. I can see a big mud slide where soft rocks are sliding down the steep cliffs into the sea.[1] The house on the top of the cliffs looks like being the next to go down the cliff, I would not like to live there. All of this is happening here because the cliffs are made out of soft rock.[2] They look to be made of sand and mud. These get wet after heavy rain which causes landslides and slumping. These are examples of mass movement which explains why the coast is being eroded.[3] Eventually after more big storms the caravan park might fall into the sea.

## Examiner's verdict

[1] The candidate is describing the physical features from the photograph, as asked for, but expression needs to be improved. Avoid 'I can see'. 'It can be seen that' is better.

[2] The candidate is starting to explain why the coast is being eroded instead of concentrating on describing what can be seen, as asked for by the question.

[3] The rest is explanation. Although geographically correct, it does not earn any marks because it is not answering the question.

**Overall**, this answer is worth 2 marks. All the marks are in the first half of the answer for physical features stated based on direct observation, such as 'mud slide', 'steep cliffs' and 'made of sand and mud'. By not focusing on answering the question set this candidate seems not to have gained a full reward for their geographical ability.

## Do better

Write an answer that will be worth all 4 marks.

4 mins

**(4 marks)**

## Question 2

With the help of an example or examples, explain why cliffs are collapsing more quickly along some stretches of coastline than along others. **(8 marks)**

### Student's answer

There are many factors that are responsible for cliffs collapsing quickly.

1 Type of rock and whether it has lots of lines of weakness like bedding planes, joints and faults or not.

2 What the waves are like. Destructive waves are more powerful than constructive waves and cause a lot of damage to coastlines made of soft rocks when they smash against them.

3 The weather. A lot depends on the weather, if is good or bad. The coastal erosion in East Anglia and the Thames estuary because gale force winds that blew from the north coincided with a high tide.

4 Humans also affect the speed of coastal erosion. In both ways, by making it worse in some places and by building sea walls and groynes in seaside resorts. This is called coastal management.

### Examiner's verdict

The candidate is attempting to answer the question by identifying factors which affect rates of coastal erosion; each of the four factors named are relevant. Also the candidate has included an example, the big storm of January 1953. It may have happened more than 50 years ago, but no storm since has caused more damage.

The layout is not the best. Continuous writing is always better, although the candidate has not made the mistake of just listing factors and saying nothing about them.

The main reason why this answer only reaches the top of Level 1 and not higher is a lack of explanation about exactly how rock types and weaknesses or people increase or decrease rates of coastal erosion. Too much is left to the examiner to work out what the candidate means.

**Overall**, top of Level 1, worth 4 marks. Grade D, almost Grade C, standard. The feeling again is that the candidate has not gained full reward for their geographical understanding.

### Do better

Write a top Level 3 answer worth all 8 marks on a separate sheet of paper.

**10 mins**

**HOW WELL DID YOU DO? SEE PAGE 117**

# Skills: Ordnance Survey maps

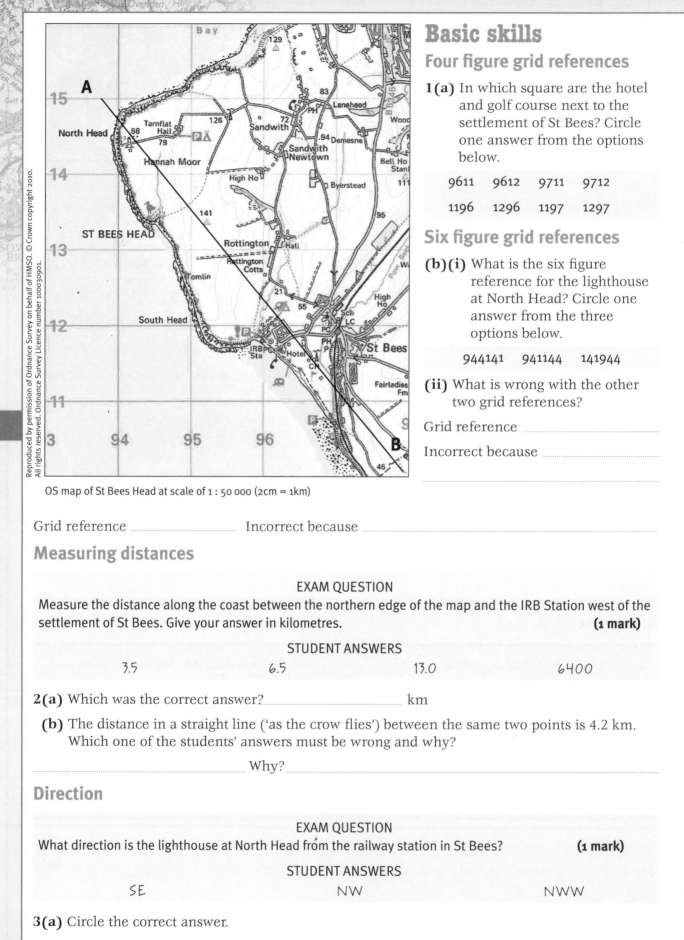

OS map of St Bees Head at scale of 1 : 50 000 (2cm = 1km)

## Basic skills

### Four figure grid references

**1(a)** In which square are the hotel and golf course next to the settlement of St Bees? Circle one answer from the options below.

| 9611 | 9612 | 9711 | 9712 |
|------|------|------|------|
| 1196 | 1296 | 1197 | 1297 |

### Six figure grid references

**(b)(i)** What is the six figure reference for the lighthouse at North Head? Circle one answer from the three options below.

944141     941144     141944

**(ii)** What is wrong with the other two grid references?

Grid reference ...............................

Incorrect because .............................

Grid reference ............................ Incorrect because .......................................

## Measuring distances

**EXAM QUESTION**

Measure the distance along the coast between the northern edge of the map and the IRB Station west of the settlement of St Bees. Give your answer in kilometres. **(1 mark)**

**STUDENT ANSWERS**

| 3.5 | 6.5 | 13.0 | 6400 |
|-----|-----|------|------|

**2(a)** Which was the correct answer? ........................... km

**(b)** The distance in a straight line ('as the crow flies') between the same two points is 4.2 km. Which one of the students' answers must be wrong and why?

..................................... Why? ...........................................

## Direction

**EXAM QUESTION**

What direction is the lighthouse at North Head from the railway station in St Bees? **(1 mark)**

**STUDENT ANSWERS**

| SE | NW | NWW |
|----|----|-----|

**3(a)** Circle the correct answer.

UNDERSTANDING GCSE GEOGRAPHY

58

**(b)** What is wrong with the other two answers?

Direction .................................... Incorrect because.........................

Direction .................................... Incorrect because.........................

## Checklist for describing relief, drainage and land use from OS maps

**4** Complete the revision checklist using the phrases in the box below.

| | | |
|---|---|---|
| river characteristics (width, straight or winding) | landforms | direction of river flow |
| vegetation (woodland type, amount) | contour patterns | heights (highest, lowest) |
| communications (roads, railway) | lakes and marsh | rivers and tributaries |
| farming, industry and recreation | steepness of slopes | settlement (rural, urban) |

| **Relief** | **Drainage** | **Land use** |
|---|---|---|
| .................................... | .................................... | .................................... |
| .................................... | .................................... | .................................... |
| .................................... | .................................... | .................................... |
| .................................... | .................................... | .................................... |

# Cross-sections and sketch maps

## Examples of sketch cross-sections

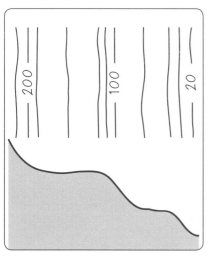 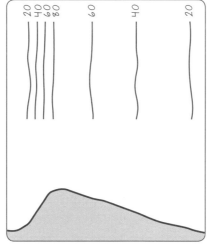

Sketch cross-sections with contours in metres.

**1** Annotate (label) the two cross-sections to describe the relief shown.

## Cross-sections

**2(a)** Annotate (label) the section below to show physical features (relief and drainage) of the cross-section A–B of the OS map extract of the St Bees area shown on page 58.

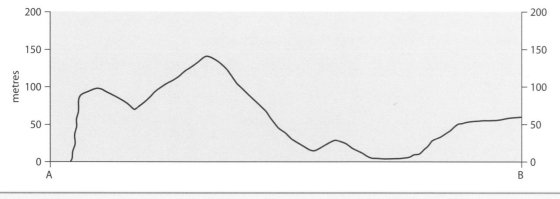

SKILLS

59

# Skills: Ordnance Survey maps

(b) Annotate (label) the section below to show human land uses of the cross-section A–B of the OS map extract of the St Bees area shown on page 58.

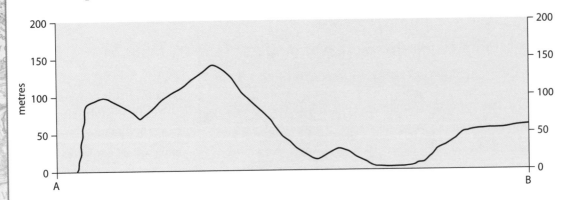

## Sketch maps and interpreting physical features

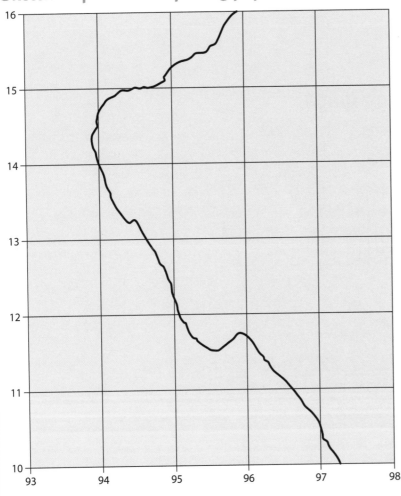

**ALTERNATIVE A**

3(a) On the map

(i) add the course of Pow Beck

(ii) mark the highest point

(iii) show a ridge-like hill top over 120 metres above sea level.

(b) Describe the physical features of the valley of Pow Beck.

.......................................................

.......................................................

.......................................................

.......................................................

.......................................................

.......................................................

.......................................................

.......................................................

.......................................................

**ALTERNATIVE B**

4(a) On the map annotate (name and label) the coastal landforms.

(b) Describe the differences between these three places: northern part of square 9515, square 9415 and square 9710.

.......................................................................................................

.......................................................................................................

.......................................................................................................

# Interpreting landforms, relief and drainage

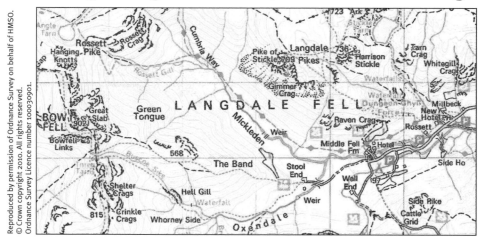

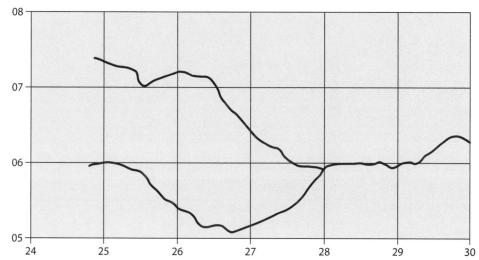

OS map of Great Langdale Valley at scale of 1:50 000 (2cm=1km)

## ALTERNATIVE C

On the map

**5(a)** add the names of the three main rivers (becks)

**(b)** show and label other drainage features of the area

**(c)** shade in the areas of flat land

**(d)** In the space below describe how the river and valley features of the Great Langdale and Mickleden Becks are different from those of the many tributary streams in the area.

SKILLS

## ALTERNATIVE D

On the map

**6(a)** shade in the areas of flat land

**(b)** mark and label 'S' an area of scree

**(c)** label and name one example of each of these glacial landforms: U-shaped valley, tarn, lake, corrie, arête, hanging valley.

**(d)** Describe the features of the Mickleden and Great Langdale valleys which show that they have been glaciated.

## Guide to answering questions for GCSE exam success

Look back at the Examiner's comments on student answers at the end of each topic, even for those topics you have not studied. What are the main messages about how and how not to answer GCSE exam questions?

**Chapter 1 The Restless Earth (pp. 8–9)**

Do not...          Do...

Question 1: describing changes between two dates (from maps)

Question 2: explaining why

**Chapter 2 Rocks, Resources and Scenery (pp. 16–7)**

Do not...          Do...

Question 1: describing landscape features from a photograph

Question 2: writing about variations (between rock types)

**Chapter 3 Challenge of Weather and Climate (pp. 24–5)**

Do not...          Do...

Question 1(a): describing climate data

Question 1(b) choosing only one from three options to write about

**Chapter 4 The Living World (pp. 32–3)**

Do not...          Do...

Question 1(b): answering a question using photographic evidence

Question 2: describing differences using suitable examples

**Chapter 5 Water on the Land (pp. 40–1)**

Do not...          Do...

Question 1(a)(ii): describing evidence from a photograph to support an answer

Question 1(b): suggesting reasons why in a 4 mark question

| **Chapter 6 Ice on the Land** (pp. 48–9) | Do not... | Do... |
|---|---|---|
| Question 1: annotating (labelling) physical features shown on a photograph | | |
| Question 2: answering an 8 mark question with two parts to it using a case study | | |

| **Chapter 7 The Coastal Zone** (pp. 56–7) | Do not... | Do... |
|---|---|---|
| Question 1: describing physical features from a photograph | | |
| Question 2: explaining in an 8 mark using examples | | |

## Summary of the main messages

- Ensure that you answer the question set.

- When describing from photographs, always make sure you focus on what can actually be seen on the photograph.

- When asked to annotate (label) make sure that you link your annotations using linking lines.

- Make best use of the space provided when answering.

- Use case study information to support your answers.

- Make sure you plan the structure of your answers to questions with 4 marks or more.

## Frequently asked questions

**Question:** How is annotating a diagram different from labelling a diagram?

**Answer:** It isn't really. Good labelling of a diagram is the same as annotation. If anything, the instruction 'annotate' implies that slightly more detail is expected, but really, in most exam questions, they come down to the same thing.

**Question:** How is annotating a diagram different from labelling a diagram?

**Question:** How do examiners mark questions which ask us to draw a labelled diagram? I am not very good at drawing diagrams.

**Answer:** Examiners are much more interested in your geographical knowledge than your artistic ability. As long as the diagram is good enough to allow the examiner to see the geographical feature shown, good labelling will gain you all the marks. A diagram must be drawn, but after that the mark scheme is biased towards rewarding appropriate geographical labels.

# Population Change

## Summary

Total world population continues to increase. While some countries are experiencing rapid population growth, many of them in Africa, in others population growth is slowing down. In a few, mainly in Europe, populations are actually declining. Problems resulting from population increase are different to those resulting from population decrease; those associated with ageing populations are spreading to more and more countries. Populations are very mobile; the impacts of people's movements, whether within or between countries, are felt in both source and receiving regions.

## Checklists for revision

| KEY IDEAS | Understand and know | Need more revision |
|---|---|---|
| **Global population increases over time** | | |
| I know reasons why the world's population is growing fast. | | |
| I understand how to work out population change (natural increase and decrease) using birth and death rates. | | |
| **The population structures of different countries change over time** | | |
| I know the differences between Stages 2, 3, 4 and 5 in the Demographic Transition Model. | | |
| I can give reasons for decreases in the rate of population growth in some countries. | | |
| I am happy describing and using population pyramids. | | |
| **Some countries experiencing rapid population growth have population policies to bring growth down** | | |
| I can describe some of the pressures caused by rapid population growth. | | |
| I can explain why some developing countries, like China, now have much lower birth rates than others, such as Niger. | | |
| **An ageing population impacts on future development of countries** | | |
| I know what is meant by an ageing population and can describe the economic problems which result. | | |
| I can name and describe one or more government strategies to cope with an ageing population. | | |
| **Population movements have effects in both the source regions of migrants and in the countries that receive them** | | |
| I can give examples of push and pull factors for migration. | | |
| I can name some of the good (positive) and bad (negative) effects of population movements into and within the EU. | | |

| CASE STUDIES – can you name an example and write about it? | | |
|---|---|---|
| **China's population policy** – strategies (methods) used, results, problems and overall effectiveness | | |
| **An EU country with an ageing population** – problems, strategies and likely effectiveness | | |

UNDERSTANDING GCSE GEOGRAPHY

**8**

# Key terms in the study of population

10 mins

| | | | |
|---|---|---|---|
| ageing population | exponential growth | population policy | annual population change |
| forced migrants | population pyramid | asylum seekers | illegal migrants |
| population structure | crude birth rate | immigration | pull factors |
| crude death rate | independent population | push factors | Demographic Transition Model |
| migration | refugees | dependants | natural decrease |
| rural–urban migration | economic migrants | natural increase | voluntary migration |
| emigration | | | |

Complete these four paragraphs by inserting each of the terms in the box once only. **(25 marks)**

Since 1950 a population explosion has raised the total world population close to 7 billion; such a rapid increase as this is known as ................................. .

The .................................... is the measure of the number of live births per 1000 people per year; the equivalent measure for deaths per 1000 people per year is the .................. ................................ . When the difference between these two measures is worked out, it tells us the ...................................... of a country, whether the country has population growth (known as .......................................) or population decline (known as ....................................). The diagram which shows changes over time by using these two measures is the ...................... ........................... . Some countries with high growth rates have a ........................................ in order to reduce future rates of growth. Other countries which have had slow growth rates for many years find that they have an increasing proportion of old people; they have an ................ .................................... .

The composition of a country's population by age and sex is known as its ............................. ........................... . The diagram which shows numbers or percentages of people in a country by age and sex is the ............................................................. . Middle-aged people (15–64) form the group which works, earns money and pays taxes; they make up the .................................... ........................... . The majority of young (0–14) and old (65 and above) rely upon services such as education and healthcare mainly paid for by taxes of working people; this is why they are referred to as .................................... .

........................................ is the movement of people. Movement of people into a country is ........................... , movement out of a country is ............................. . People move and change homes for a complex mixture of factors; those that drive people out from a place are called ..................................., whereas ............................... are those that attract someone to a place. Many people make their own decisions when and where to move, which is why this is called .................................... . For example, in the developing world there is a mass movement of people from farms to cities, ........................................................ . Young adults are the ones most likely to move in order to seek work in other countries; because the purpose of the migration is to make more money, these people are .................................... . Totally different are those people who have no choice but to move due to war or natural disaster; they are .................................... . Those among them who see no alternative but leave for another country are ....................................... . Some individuals manage to enter countries without valid entry documents, such as North Africans into southern Italy; they are ............................... . Others, who are detained at entry points by customs officials and need to make a case to be allowed to stay in the country are ....................................... .

# Population growth and change

 10 mins

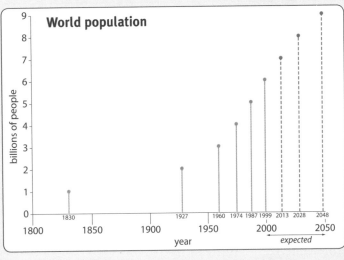

World population

## World population growth

1 On the graph

  **(a)** draw the line to show world population growth

  **(b)** shade in between the two dates with the lowest time for a one billion population increase.

  **(c)** State the graph evidence that world population growth has peaked.

.................................................................

## Factors leading to a fall in birth rate

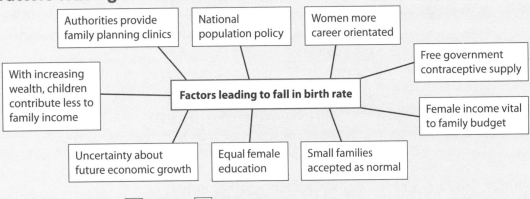

| | | |
|---|---|---|
| Authorities provide family planning clinics | National population policy | Women more career orientated |
| | | Free government contraceptive supply |
| With increasing wealth, children contribute less to family income | **Factors leading to fall in birth rate** | Female income vital to family budget |
| Uncertainty about future economic growth | Equal female education | Small families accepted as normal |

**Key** ☐ Economic    ☐ Social    ☐ Political

2 Shade or colour each factor according to whether it is economic, social or political, and complete the key.

## Demographic Transition Model

3 **(a)** On the sketch, shade or colour in where natural increase and natural decrease in population are shown, and complete the key.

**(b)** Fill in the table below using information from the graph to help.

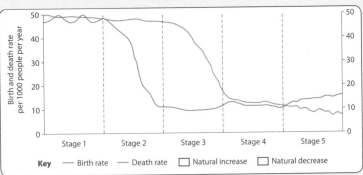

Key   — Birth rate   — Death rate   ☐ Natural increase   ☐ Natural decrease

| | Key change shown between the two stages | BR/DR values showing this change | Factors responsible for this change |
|---|---|---|---|
| From 1–2 | | | |
| From 2–3 | | | |
| From 3–4 | | | |
| From 4–5 | | | |

# Population structures

**Ethiopia**

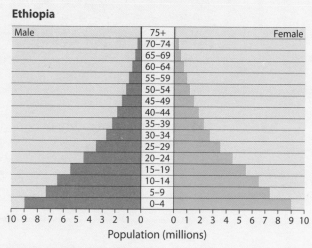

**UK**

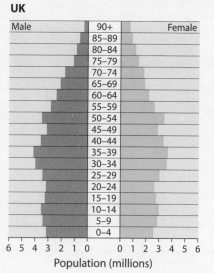

## Population pyramids

**1** On both graphs

    **(a)** draw lines across to divide into age groups (young, middle-aged and old)

    **(b)** label the independent and dependent populations.

**2** Fill in the table to describe how the pyramids show typical population structures for developing and developed countries.

| Typical pyramid characteristics | Ethiopia economically developing country | UK economically developed country |
|---|---|---|
| Base | | |
| Overall shape | | |
| Top | | |
| DTM | Stage number: | Stage number: |

**3 (a)** From the pyramid for Ethiopia, work out the approximate percentages of

    **(i)** young people (under 15) ................. %  **(ii)** old people (65 and above) .................. %

    **(iii)** people of working age (15–64) .................. %

**(b)** Use the percentages to fill in the boxes below and calculate the dependency ratio for Ethiopia.

$$\frac{\text{\% of non-workers}}{\text{\% of workers}} = \frac{\boxed{\phantom{xx}}}{\boxed{\phantom{xx}}} = \boxed{\phantom{xx}} \% \qquad \text{ratio of workers } \boxed{\phantom{xx}} : 1 \text{ non-workers}$$

**4 (a)** Calculate the UK dependency ratios for

|  | 1940 | 1980 | 2009 | 2031 (est.) |
|---|---|---|---|---|
| Under 15 | 24 | 19 | 19 | 18 |
| Working age | 66 | 69 | 62 | 60 |
| 65 and above | 10 | 12 | 19 | 22 |

Population structure of UK (percentages)

    **(i)** 1940: workers $\boxed{\phantom{xx}}$ : 1 non-workers

    **(ii)** 2031 (estimated): workers $\boxed{\phantom{xx}}$ : 1 non-workers

**(b)** Explain why the UK's population is described as 'ageing'. ...................................................

...........................................................................

...........................................................................

# Migration

10 mins

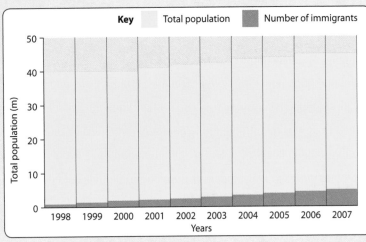

**Immigrants in Spain (1998–2007)**

1 Describe what the graph shows about:

(a) total numbers of immigrants in Spain

........................................................

........................................................

(b) immigrants as a proportion of total population.

........................................................

........................................................

........................................................

........................................................

2 Use the items in the boxes to complete the two flow graphs – to show differences in migration between good and bad economic times in Spain.

| **Good economic times** |
| --- |
| Rapid transformation and growth of cities (e.g. Barcelona) and tourist areas (e.g. Costa del Sol) |
| Immigrants are cheap labour for building sites, hotels, etc. |
| Immigrants from EU, North Africa and South America welcomed |
| Large numbers of workers needed, and fast |

| **Bad economic times** |
| --- |
| Social unrest and street demonstrations for government to cut visas for more migrants |
| Rising pressure on government to send immigrants back to their home countries |
| Rising rates of unemployment after years of labour shortages (10%) |
| Recession worsens leading to more cutbacks by businesses and record unemployment (20%) |

**Booming economy 1998–2007**

Construction, tourism and other sectors are booming

**Recession 2008 – ?**

Recession halts construction and other new projects

3 Fill the spaces suggesting reasons why people have different opinions about migration.

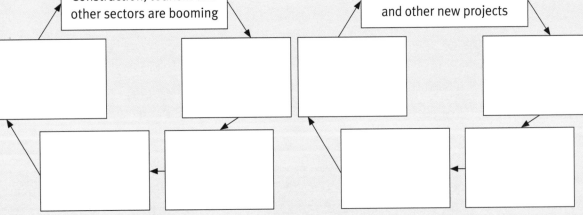

| **Fruit farmer near Hereford** |
| --- |
| • Employs pickers from Poland and Latvia at harvest times for apples and strawberries. |
| • Claims that he can no longer find English people willing to do the work. |

**Attitudes of local people**

Disapprove ...................................................

........................................................

Approve ...................................................

........................................................

## CHINA'S POPULATION POLICY

**Strategies (methods) used**

........................................................................

........................................................................

........................................................................

........................................................................

........................................................................

**Positive results**

........................................................................

........................................................................

........................................................................

**Drawbacks and problems**

........................................................................

........................................................................

........................................................................

........................................................................

**Overall effectiveness**

........................................................................

........................................................................

........................................................................

## EU COUNTRY WITH AN AGEING POPULATION

Name of country ..................................................

**Problems caused**

........................................................................

........................................................................

........................................................................

........................................................................

........................................................................

**Strategies for coping with problems**

........................................................................

........................................................................

........................................................................

........................................................................

**Likely future effectiveness**

........................................................................

........................................................................

........................................................................

## COUNTRY WITH A NON-BIRTH CONTROL POPULATION POLICY (IE NO REAL POLICY)

Name of country ..................................................

**Policy/plan in existence** ................................

........................................................................

**Why badly needed** ............................................

........................................................................

........................................................................

**Problems for policy introduction**

........................................................................

........................................................................

........................................................................

## EU COUNTRY WITH IN-MIGRATION

Name of country ..................................................

**Main source countries for in-migration**

........................................................................

........................................................................

**Positive effects of in-migration**

........................................................................

........................................................................

**Negative effects of in-migration**

........................................................................

........................................................................

# GradeStudio

## PRACTICE GCSE QUESTIONS

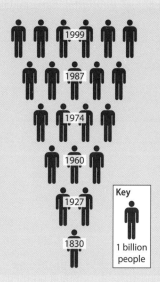

**Figure 1**

Key
1 billion people

### Question 1

**Figure 1** shows total world population between 1830 and 1999.

Describe what **Figure 1** shows about the rate of world population growth. **(3 marks)**

## Student's answer

Figure 1 shows total world population at five dates between 1830 and 1999. **1**

In 1830 there were only 1 billion people. By 1927 total world population had grown to 2 billion. It just kept on growing and growing to 3 billion in 1960, then 4 billion in 1974, 5 billion in 1987 and finally 6 billion by 1999. **2** All of this shows that it grew a lot between 1830 and 1999. This is what Figure 1 shows. **3**

## Examiner's verdict

**1** Repeating information given – a waste of time and space.

**2** Stating total world populations shown at the different dates, but how relevant is this to a question about rate of world population growth?

**3** Still nothing about rate of growth. Information from the pictograph has not been used in a manner that answers the question set.

**Overall**, no marks. There is nothing about rate of growth i.e. the relative speed of growth, and how the graph shows that this changed over time. Although values from the graph have been stated, they have not be used to answer the question set. Did the student not read the question carefully enough before answering? Or did they not understand what is meant by rate of growth?

## Do better

Write an answer that does answer the question set and is worth 3 marks.

4 mins

**(3 marks)**

## Question 2

Explain why the effectiveness of national population policies to reduce growth varies greatly between countries. Refer to examples to support your answer. **(6 marks)**

### Student's answer

One country with a national population policy that has reduced population growth is China. This is the famous one child policy. Couples must have no more children after they have had their first child. If they do, they are criticised by local officials and fined. Those couples with two children lose many privileges, no free education, no allowances, no pension benefits. Before they marry couples must be at least 20 and they need the permission of local officials. The Chinese government provides free family planning and does not accept excuses for a couple having a second child. The policy has been a great success in stopping rapid population growth. Its total population has grown only slowly from 1.2. billion to 1.3 billion. It is still the country with most people in the world but might be overtaken by India soon, with a much less strongly enforced population policy. The Chinese policy has been so effective because China has a strong communist government. The policy is very unpopular with most Chinese people but the government stops all protests against it

### Examiner's verdict

Good student knowledge of China's one child national population policy is shown. But has the student used this knowledge in the best way to answer the question set? The question theme is variations in effectiveness between countries. By referring only to one country, the theme of variations between countries is not being tackled.

Can you see where the student had the big opportunity to move the answer closer to the question? This came with the mention of India. If only the student had begun to explain why India's population policy is not as strong and could not be implemented with the same ruthlessness as in China. Using examples of other countries with weak or non-existent policies, such as Niger or Saudi Arabia, would have considerably raised the standard of the answer as well.

**Overall,** this just creeps into the bottom half of Level 2 and is worth 3 marks at best. Only Grade D standard. Make sure you answer the question; only then do you stand a chance of having your geographical knowledge fully rewarded.

### Do better

Improve this answer; make use of some of the content if you wish. Convert it into a top Level 3 answer worth 6 marks. Write your improved answer on a separate piece of lined paper.

6 mins

# Changing Urban Environments

## Summary

For the first time in human history more people now live in cities than in the countryside. The world's big cities are growing fast, especially in the developing world, where rapid urbanisation has led to the growth of squatter settlements. The layout of land uses within urban areas leads to distinctive urban zones such as city centre (CBD), inner city and suburbs. Urban problems, especially housing, traffic, and pollution need careful planning and management. Some attempts are being made to try to make urban living more sustainable.

## Checklists for revision

| KEY IDEAS | Understand and know | Need more revision |
|---|---|---|
| **Urbanisation is a global phenomenon, but the speed of growth is greater in poor world countries** | | |
| I can explain why big cities are growing faster in poor than in rich countries. | | |
| **Urban areas have a variety of land uses which cluster together to give distinctive urban zones** | | |
| I can describe changes in land uses between city centre and city edges in British cities. | | |
| I know two ways in which the layout of cities in the the poorer part of the world world is different. | | |
| **Cities in the richer part of the world need careful planning to improve urban living** | | |
| I can give information about examples of inner city improvement in UK cities. | | |
| I know three ways for reducing the amount of traffic entering city centres. | | |
| **Rapid city growth in the poorer part of the world has led to the growth of squatter settlements** | | |
| I can describe the characteristics of squatter settlements. | | |
| I can explain how squatter settlements can be improved to become proper residential areas. | | |
| **Management of the environmental problems caused by rapid urbanisation in the developing world is needed** | | |
| I can describe three environmental problems caused by rapid city growth in the developing world. | | |
| I can explain how these problems can be managed to reduce their effects. | | |
| **Attempts can be made to ensure that urban living is sustainable** | | |
| I can describe three ways of making urban living more sustainable. | | |

| CASE STUDIES – can you name an example and write about it? | | |
|---|---|---|
| **Squatter settlement redevelopment** – location, changes and results | | |
| **Sustainable urban living** – location, changes and what makes it sustainable | | |

# Quick test – urban land uses and layout

 **10 mins**

| | | |
|---|---|---|
| business and commerce | CBD | commuter (suburbanised) village |
| detached houses | housing people (residential) | inner city |
| industrial zone | large shops and stores | low value old housing |
| making and distributing goods | old historical buildings | out-of-town shopping centre |
| residential suburbs | rural–urban fringe | semi-detached houses |
| shacks and slum housing | squatter settlements | terraced housing |
| skyscraper offices | tower blocks of flats | factories and warehousing |

Fill in the answers using items from the box; some may be used more than once, others not at all. Only in part **1(d)** do you need to add something of your own in order to explain why.

## 1 UK cities

```
          A     B                    C          Edge of      D
City  |---+----------+----------------------------+..................|
centre                                     built-up area
```

**(a)** Name the zones on the transect line from centre to edge in a British city.   **(4 marks)**

A ............................................................   B ............................................................

C ............................................................   D ............................................................

**(b)** Name two land uses in each zone. **(4 marks)**

| A | B | C | D |
|---|---|---|---|
| | | | |
| | | | |

**(c)** Name the main function of zones A and C.  **(2 marks)**

A ............................................................   C ............................................................

**(d)** Identify the zone worst affected by these urban problems and explain why.   **(6 marks)**

| | Zone | Why |
|---|---|---|
| Traffic congestion | | |
| Old and poor quality housing | | |
| Ethnic segregation | | |

## 2 Developing world cities

```
          A      B              C  Edge of formal       D
City  |----+----------------+---------------+................................|
centre                                    built-up area
```

**(a)** Name the zones on the transect line from centre to edge in a developing world city.

**(4 marks)**

A ............................................................   B ............................................................

C ............................................................   D ............................................................

**(b)** Name the main land use in, and function of, each zone.   **(4 marks)**

| A | B | C | D |
|---|---|---|---|

Land use ............................................................................................

Function ............................................................................................

# Urban growth – the big switch from developed to developing worlds

**10 mins**

## World urban population (1950–2010)

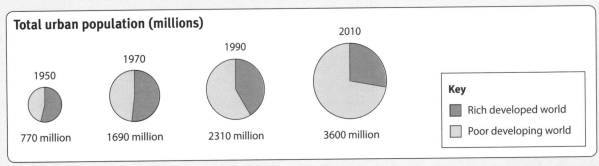

**1 (a)** From 1950, how many times (approximately) had total world urban population increased

**(i)** by 1970 ............................ **(ii)** by 1990 ............................ **(iii)** by 2010? ............................ **(3 marks)**

**(b)** Describe how the distribution of urban population between the richer and poorer parts of the world changed over the years from 1950 to 2010.

..............................................................................................................................................................

.......................................................................................................................................... **(3 marks)**

## Location of the world's top 10 biggest cities (1950 and 2005)

**2 (a)** On the world map, name the six inhabited continents in the spaces provided. **(3 marks)**

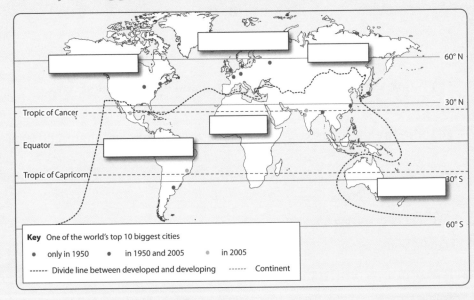

**(b)** Describe the location of the five cities that had dropped out of the top 10 by 2005 in relation to

**(i)** latitude ............................................................................................................. **(2 marks)**

**(ii)** wealth ............................................................................................................. **(1 mark)**

**(c)** Describe the distribution of the top ten biggest cities in 2005 in relation to

**(i)** latitude ............................................................................................................. **(2 marks)**

**(ii)** wealth ............................................................................................................. **(2 marks)**

**(iii)** continents ............................................................................................................. **(2 marks)**

**3** How are the pie graphs and world map related?

..............................................................................................................................................................

.......................................................................................................................................... **(2 marks)**

# Urban issues and problems – strategies for management

**Traffic – in all big cities:** rush hour congestion, air pollution, high human health risks

**Main causes:** high car ownership, old vehicles poorly maintained, main work places located in city cities where narrow streets with tall buildings trap pollutants

**Strategies for management** – describe how each of the following can help:

- banning old vehicles
- better public transport
- use of new fuels
- restricted entry into centres
- by-passes and motorways

**Difficulties for implementing them?**

**Housing – in developing world cities:** squatter settlements, slums without basic amenities, health and other social problems

**Main causes:** high rates of natural increase, mass migration from rural to urban areas

**Strategies and solutions** – describe how each of the following can help:

- Self Help
- Site and Service (help from Authorities on site)

- Local Authority Schemes

**Difficulties for implementing them?**

**Housing – in the UK:** housing shortages, poor quality housing, ethnic segregation, land pressures on the countryside for greenfield sites

**Main causes:** population increase, more people living alone, growth of multicultural society, old housing stock

**Strategies and solutions** – describe how each of the following can help:

- City Challenge (e.g. Hulme in Manchester)

- Brownfield site redevelopment schemes (e.g. dockland areas)

**Difficulties for implementing them?**

# Sustainable urban living

10 mins

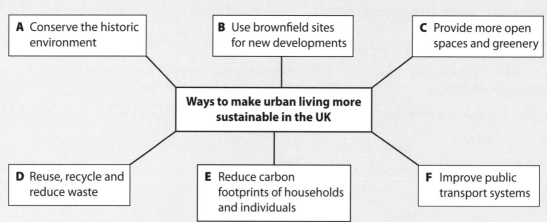

**A** Conserve the historic environment

**B** Use brownfield sites for new developments

**C** Provide more open spaces and greenery

**Ways to make urban living more sustainable in the UK**

**D** Reuse, recycle and reduce waste

**E** Reduce carbon footprints of households and individuals

**F** Improve public transport systems

1  Read the examples of sustainable urban change below. Give the letters of the ways of making urban living more sustainable in the spider diagram that they meet.

**Letters**

(a) Shells of old warehouses converted into new apartments

...................................

(b) Sides of canals, rivers and railways landscaped and made into walkways and cycleways

...................................

(c) Homes with high levels of roof and wall insulation, solar panels on roofs and smart meters for energy use

...................................

(d) Bus, tram and rail powered by electricity and CNG (compressed natural gas), linked at interchanges

...................................

2  Describe how the examples of unsustainable urban living below can be made more sustainable.

| Unsustainable | More sustainable |
|---|---|
| (a) Knock down old buildings, bulldoze the sites, burn wood and other flammable materials on site, take rubble away and dump it in landfill sites. | |
| (b) Use the car as the main means of transport for commuting to work, local journeys to schools and shops, and for leisure use. | |
| (c) Planning permission for Green Belt land in the rural–urban fringe to be developed for new housing, out-of-town shopping centres, business parks and motorway interchanges. | |
| (d) High household energy use, in old houses and flats with high heat losses and with wasteful consumption. | |

## SQUATTER SETTLEMENT REDEVELOPMENT

Name and location ............................................
................................................................

**Characteristics**
................................................................
................................................................
................................................................

**Changes and improvements made**
................................................................
................................................................
................................................................
................................................................

**What made them possible and results**
................................................................
................................................................
................................................................
................................................................
................................................................

## SUSTAINABLE URBAN LIVING

Name and location ............................................
................................................................

**Characteristics**
................................................................
................................................................
................................................................
................................................................
................................................................
................................................................
................................................................

**What makes it sustainable**
................................................................
................................................................
................................................................
................................................................

## EXAMPLE: INNER CITY IMPROVEMENT IN THE UK

Location ............................................................

**Before**
................................................................
................................................................
................................................................
................................................................

**After**
................................................................
................................................................
................................................................
................................................................

**Overall assessment**
................................................................
................................................................
................................................................
................................................................

## EXAMPLE: ATTEMPTS TO SOLVE URBAN PROBLEMS IN A DEVELOPING WORLD CITY

Name of city ......................................................

**Problem** .......................................................

Attempted solution ..........................................
................................................................
................................................................

**Problem** .......................................................

Attempted solution ..........................................
................................................................
................................................................

**Problem** .......................................................

Attempted solution ..........................................
................................................................
................................................................

# GradeStudio

## PRACTICE GCSE QUESTIONS

### Question 1

Study the photograph of a housing area located on the edge of the built-up area of Cape Town in South Africa. Describe the characteristics of the housing area shown in the photograph. **(4 marks)**

## Student's answer

If this housing area is on the edge of the built-up area of Cape Town,

then it must be a squatter settlement. This is an area of slum housing.

They are built on any spare land that people new to the city can find.

These are poor people from the countryside and they are left to build their own

houses using any materials they can find like wood, tin sheets and plastic.

Their houses are often without services like electricity and running water.

## Examiner's verdict

Hasn't the student answered this question, '*Describe the characteristics of a squatter settlement*', instead of the question set? Can you see anything in this answer that is definitely description from the photograph? The student probably took a quick look at the photograph, decided that it showed a squatter settlement, correctly, but then started to write using knowledge rather than observation.

**Overall**, 1 mark only. Details about the materials used to build the houses do match those that can be seen in the photograph, but how the student wrote the answer did not suggest to the examiner that it was description from the photo.

## Do better

Write an answer based on the photograph worthy of 4 marks.

4 mins

(4 marks)

## Question 2

Describe the environmental problems created by rapid urbanisation in poor world cities and briefly explain why they are difficult to manage. **(6 marks)**

## Student's answer

The main environmental problems are traffic congestion leading to air pollution, water pollution and over-use of water stores for water supplies. Traffic greatly increases with urban growth. Many cars, buses and trucks are too old to have had catalytic converters fitted. They belch out plumes of fumes. Their effects are worse in big cities like Mexico City with a population close to 20 million, because fumes are trapped by the surrounding mountains, and the dry climate means there is not much rain to wash all the pollutants away. In Beijing industries burning low-grade coal make the pollution worse, which is why people wear nose masks to reduce damage to chest and lungs. Factory owners often flout regulations by discharging waste directly into rivers. Slums without sewage systems are often found next to water courses, which become open sewers without plant and fish life. Because river water is no good to drink, some cities like Mexico City are overusing underground water stores, which are dropping lower and lower. Three reasons explain why these problems are difficult to solve. They are high cost, size of the problem getting worse *(Extra space)* as more people come into the city, and lack of rule enforcement. Cairo has done more to manage its problems than a lot of big cities, with its new metro, extending the sewer system and building new towns, but effectiveness of all of them is limited by its continuing fast growth.

## Examiner's verdict

Top of Level 3, full marks. There is no such thing as a 'model answer'. Every full mark answer that examiners read is different. What this student has done is to write the type of answer that most A* grade students would be expected to write.

**Why is this a very good answer?**

Read the examiner's mark scheme for a Level 3 answer.

**Level 3 (Detailed) 5–6 marks**

Description of two or more environmental problems, with some development.

Some appropriate explanation of the difficulties of management.

Well written organised answer; quality perhaps helped by use of named examples. **(6 marks)**

Identify examples from the student's answer where the requirements for a top Level 3 answer were met.

Description of two or more environmental problems with some development ............................................

**6 mins**

Difficulties of management explained ............................................

Quality helped by use of named examples ............................................

Answer well written and organised because ............................................

**HOW WELL DID YOU DO? SEE PAGE 118**

# Changing Rural Environments

## Summary

The rural–urban fringe in the UK is under great pressure from urban sprawl. Increased mobility has led to remote rural areas undergoing social and economic changes as well. The challenge is to ensure that rural living remains sustainable with its own services and work. There are great commercial pressures on farming in the UK, many of them encouraging more intensive farming, with consequences for the environment. Likewise in rural areas of tropical countries, commercial pressures are being felt more and more strongly, with impacts on subsistence food production and the environment.

## Checklists for revision

| KEY IDEAS | Understand and know | Need more revision |
|---|---|---|
| **The rural–urban fringe is under great pressure from urban sprawl** | | |
| I know what is meant by rural–urban fringe. | | |
| I can give reasons why villages in rural areas close to cities are growing in population and expanding in size. | | |
| I can state the main characteristics of expanding, suburbanised villages. | | |
| **Remote rural areas have undergone social and economic changes** | | |
| I can state the characteristics of villages in decline. | | |
| **Attempts should be made to ensure that rural living is sustainable** | | |
| I can describe three ways of making rural living more sustainable for the future. | | |
| **Commercial agriculture in favoured agricultural areas is influenced by human needs and pressures** | | |
| I know what is meant by agri-businesses. | | |
| I can name three ways in which intensive farming in the UK damages the environment. | | |
| I can name and explain EU and UK government policies to reduce environmental damage from intensive farming. | | |
| **Rural areas in the tropics and sub-tropics are increasingly subject to change and conflict** | | |
| I can state the causes and impact of soil erosion in tropical and sub-tropical areas. | | |
| I know what is meant by appropriate technology and how it can help poor people in tropical areas. | | |

| CASE STUDIES – can you name an example and write about it? | | |
|---|---|---|
| **Rural area in the UK** – rural depopulation reasons and consequences, characteristics of declining villages, growth of second homes | | |
| **Commercial farming area in the UK** – favourable factors, agri-business and its environmental effects, changes | | |

# Quick test – rural settlement and farming

 **10 mins**

## 1 Settlement in the UK

| | | |
|---|---|---|
| commuter village | greenfield sites/Green Belt | out-of-town shopping centre |
| rural depopulation | second homes | shops, post offices, schools closing |

Choose from the list above the **best match** to each of the following. Choose also the most likely location. **(6 marks)**

| | Best match | Rural–urban fringe, or remote rural area? |
|---|---|---|
| Retail park | ............................. | ............................. |
| Suburbanised village | ............................. | ............................. |
| Rural to urban migration | ............................. | ............................. |
| Holiday homes | ............................. | ............................. |
| Decline in rural services | ............................. | ............................. |
| Under pressure due to urban sprawl | ............................. | ............................. |

## 2 Farming in the UK and the tropics

| | | |
|---|---|---|
| development of agri-business | high impact on the environment | soil erosion |
| small-scale family farming | farming, forestry, sometimes mining | sustainable farming |

Choose from the list above the **best match** to each of the following. Choose also the most likely location. **(6 marks)**

| | Best match | UK, or tropics and sub-tropics? |
|---|---|---|
| Large scale commercial farming | ............................. | ............................. |
| Subsistence production | ............................. | ............................. |
| Over-use of land by farmers | ............................. | ............................. |
| Modern farming practices | ............................. | ............................. |
| Use of appropriate technology developments | ............................. | ............................. |
| Rural economy/activities | ............................. | ............................. |

## 3 Farming opposites: key terms from the specification

| | | | |
|---|---|---|---|
| agri-business | appropriate technology | cash crop farming | modern farming practices |
| failing agricultural systems | global food market | high environmental impact farming | organic farming |

Write each of the key terms in the space below its best-fitting opposite. **(8 marks)**

**(a)** subsistence food production

..........................................

**(b)** chemicals – fertilisers and pesticides

..........................................

**(c)** traditional family farming

..........................................

**(d)** environmental stewardship scheme

..........................................

**(e)** surplus to local market

..........................................

**(f)** large dam irrigation project

..........................................

**(g)** using animals to plough

..........................................

**(h)** expanding profitable farming

..........................................

# Declining and expanding villages in the UK

**10 mins**

Give the information requested and fill in any empty boxes.

## Declining villages

**Decline in rural employment**

Causes of decline in farming

........................................................
........................................................
........................................................
........................................................

Causes of decline
in mining

........................................................
........................................................
........................................................
........................................................

**Examples of areas in the UK**

........................................................

| Decline in rural employment |

| Fewer employment opportunities |

| Ageing population |

| Rural–urban migration |

| Lower rate of natural increase |

| More young people leave village |

**Leading to:
decline in services**

Examples

........................................................
........................................................

Because

........................................................
........................................................
........................................................
........................................................

**increase in second homes**

Because

........................................................
........................................................
........................................................

## Expanding villages

**Increase in rural living**

Causes of growth in commuting

........................................................
........................................................

Reasons why there is
more desire to live in
rural areas

........................................................
........................................................
........................................................
........................................................
........................................................

**Examples of areas in the UK**

........................................................

| Increase in rural living |

| Old houses renovated and extended, new houses built |

**Resulting in changes**

Environmental

........................................................
........................................................

Social

........................................................
........................................................

Services

........................................................
........................................................

# Commercial farming and agri-business in the UK – quick summary

10 mins

## Agri-business characteristics

Circle the correct answer or cross out the wrong answer.

| | |
|---|---|
| **Scale of farming** | small/large |
| **Business efficiency** | low/high |
| **Farm size** | decreasing/increasing |
| **Farming intensity** | low/high |
| **Farming inputs** | low/high |
| **Machinery use** | little/great |
| **Labour need** | low/high |
| **Output/yields** | low/high |
| **Importance of market** | low/high |

## Main markets for produce

What demands do supermarkets and food producing companies make on the farmers?

Quality

Amount

Freshness

Why are chemicals (fertilisers and pesticides) used on most farms?

## Agri-business changes and effects

1  Non-productive land such as hedgerows, wetland and patches of woodland are changed into farmland. The result is increased farm output from:

**(a)** extra land area

**(b)** easier use of machinery because

2  Explain the increased environmental impact for

**(a)** the soil

**(b)** water (surface and underground)

**(c)** wildlife

## Government/EU policies to reduce environmental effects

Environmental stewardship scheme – farmers are paid to

**(a)** leave wider gap between hedgerows and cropland – why?

**(b)** leave stubble in cornfields over winter – why ?

**(c)** start grass cutting for silage and hay later in the summer – why?

## Organic farming compared with agri-business

Its advantage

Its disadvantages

# Change in rural areas of the tropics and sub-tropics (0–30° N&S)

## Impact of soil erosion

1  Add labels to the photograph to show **(a)** why the risk of soil erosion in this area is high and **(b)** what farmers are doing to reduce the risk.

## Sustainable and unsustainable ways of using the land

2  Fill in the boxes by answering the questions.

| **Why is the following sustainable?** | **Why is the following unsustainable?** |
|---|---|
| Subsistence food production by tribes in the Amazon Basin using shifting cultivation | Clearing rainforest in the Amazon Basin for commercial farming (soya and cattle ranching) |

| **What problems does this unsustainable practice cause?** | **Why does the following represent sustainable development?** |
|---|---|
| Large-scale irrigation – large dam, river and canal transfers, surface channels between crops, all year use of land for crop growing | Appropriate technology – small earth dams on nearby streams, rainwater collection, trickle drip irrigation, advice on soil conservation |

## RURAL AREA IN THE UK

Name of area and location within UK ....................................................................................................

**Reason for rural depopulation**

..........................................................................................................................................................................

..........................................................................................................................................................................

..........................................................................................................................................................................

**Consequences of rural depopulation**

..........................................................................................................................................................................

..........................................................................................................................................................................

..........................................................................................................................................................................

**Characteristics of declining villages**

..........................................................................................................................................................................

..........................................................................................................................................................................

..........................................................................................................................................................................

**Reasons for growth of second homes**

..........................................................................................................................................................................

..........................................................................................................................................................................

..........................................................................................................................................................................

**10**

CASE STUDIES

## COMMERCIAL FARMING AREA IN THE UK

Name of area and location within UK ....................................................................................................

**Favourable factors for farming**

Physical ..........................................................................................................................................................

Human ............................................................................................................................................................

**Details about the development of agri-business**

..........................................................................................................................................................................

..........................................................................................................................................................................

**Farming impacts on the environment**

..........................................................................................................................................................................

..........................................................................................................................................................................

..........................................................................................................................................................................

**Changes due to market demands and government policies**

..........................................................................................................................................................................

..........................................................................................................................................................................

..........................................................................................................................................................................

# GCSE EXAM QUESTIONS AND ANSWERS FROM DIFFERENT STUDENTS

## Question 1

Describe the typical characteristics of a declining village in the UK.　　**(4 marks)**

## Student's answer

- Bad housing
- 2nd homes owned by city folk
- Lots of old people living in it
- Village looks bad [1]

This is because so many people have left and moved to live in towns and cities. For more [2] work and better pay. Young people get bored because there is nothing to do.

## Examiner's verdict

[1] In a list; a poor arrangement, without any attempt to describe the characteristics more fully.

Poor and limited use of language – what is meant by bad housing or the village looking bad?

[2] No longer describing, starting instead to explain village characteristics (albeit very poorly). The general rule is that examiners ignore anything not asked for by the question.

**Overall**, a level 1 performance, worth 1 mark only for identifying two valid characteristics (poor housing and ageing population). Additional description is totally lacking, and the language is not very geographical! The last two lines contain nothing relevant.

## Do better

Write an answer which fully answers the question set. Bearing in mind that this question is worth 4 marks, you should be looking to identify and describe a minimum of three different characteristics of declining villages.

**4 mins**

**(3 marks)**

## Question 2

Some villages in rural areas of the UK are growing while others are declining.
Using example(s), give reasons for this. **(6 marks)**

### Student's answer

In my opinion village location matters most. Villages that are close to big cities, with plenty of different types of work, that are easy to reach by road or rail, are the ones that are most likely to change from being farming villages and to grow into commuter villages. Other villages located 20 or 30 or more miles away from a town, in upland areas, with nothing better than slow B class road links to them are the ones most likely to decline. A good example of a growing village is Shincliffe. A few miles to the west is Durham City, where many work in the University, prisons and County Hall. Not far to the east is the A1 motorway for commuting by car to Newcastle and Gateshead. Surrounded by woods, farms and fields you can hardly tell that it was once a coal mining village. Other old Durham mining villages further away from cities are declining. Some like Ferryhill Station (station closed in 1960s) still have eyesores from coal mining with old pit heaps and rows of terraced houses that are gradually being knocked down. In Metal Bridge only a few houses are left.     **(6 marks)**

### Examiner's verdict

A very good answer because the student

- refers to a range of relevant factors including location in relation to urban areas and transport links, employment opportunities and attractiveness or otherwise of the environment.

- uses very suitable examples of growing and declining villages to illustrate these factors.

- writes a direct answer to the question which is easy to follow.

**Overall,** a top Level 3 answer – as good as can be expected from a GCSE student in the time available. This student makes good use of local examples. It is always best to use local examples in answers whenever they exist. Here the student leaves the examiner with the feeling that they could have written much more about them if needed.

### Do as well as this student

There are many different ways of writing a six mark answer. Write an answer of your own that is equally good and worth 6 marks using the example(s) that you have studied. Write your answer on a separate piece of lined paper.

6 mins

**HOW WELL DID YOU DO? SEE PAGE 118**

# The Development Gap

## Summary

Countries are at different levels of economic development. A simple global divide is between developed countries in the North and developing countries in the South, based on high standards of living in North America, Europe and Australasia, and lower quality of life in much of Asia, South America, and Africa. The gap between the two worlds is widening due to a mixture of physical and human factors. International efforts to narrow the gap include Fair Trade and aid for sustainable development projects. Within the enlarged EU, there are also wide variations in levels of development between countries.

## Checklists for revision

| KEY IDEAS | Understand and know | Need more revision |
|---|---|---|
| **Contrasts in development can be used to divide up the world in many ways** | | |
| I can name and explain at least three different ways of measuring the development gap between countries. | | |
| I know what is meant by quality of life and can describe how it can be improved. | | |
| **Global inequalities between rich and poor are increasing due to physical and human factors** | | |
| I can give the causes and impact of a natural disaster in a developing country. | | |
| I can explain how the pattern of world trade favours developed at the expense of developing countries. | | |
| I understand the problems caused by poor access to clean water supplies. | | |
| **International efforts are needed to reduce these global inequalities** | | |
| I can describe ways of making world trade fairer to developing countries. | | |
| I know what is meant by development aid and can state some of its differences and advantages compared with other types of aid. | | |
| **Countries within the EU show contrasting levels of development, which have led to a number of initiatives to reduce inequalities** | | |
| I know the distribution of more wealthy and less wealthy countries within the enlarged EU. | | |
| I can describe ways in which the EU is trying to reduce differences in levels of development between member countries. | | |

| CASE STUDIES – can you name an example of each and write about it? | | |
|---|---|---|
| **One natural hazard** – name and location, cause, impact, responses <br> Example ................................................. | | |
| **One development project** – name and location, project information, changes and results <br> Example ................................................. | | |
| **Two contrasting EU countries for levels of development** – names contrasting locations, measures of development, causes <br> Examples ........................... and ................ | | |

# Quick test – measures of development

10 mins

## GNP, GNI, HDI

**1 (a)** Write out what each one stands for.

GNI ................................................................

GNP ................................................................ HDI ................................................ **(3 marks)**

**(b)** What is the similarity between GNP and GNI?

........................................................................................................................................ **(1 mark)**

**(c)** How is HDI different from the other two?

........................................................................................................................................ **(1 mark)**

**(d)(i)** What is the difference between **standard of living** and **quality of life**?

........................................................................................................................................ **(1 mark)**

**(ii)** How are these two related?

........................................................................................................................................ **(1 mark)**

## Other measures of development

| | | | |
|---|---|---|---|
| access to safe water | birth rate | death rate | infant mortality |
| life expectancy | literacy rate | people per doctor | |

**2** Select the measure of development from the box which matches the average values, and state whether they are high or low averages for developing and developed countries. Two have already been done for you. **(5 marks)**

| Measure of development | World averages | | | High or low | |
|---|---|---|---|---|---|
| | Developing | Developed | Unit | Developing | Developed |
| | 26 | 12 | per 1000 | | |
| death rate | 9 | 10 | per 1000 | low | low |
| | 64 | 14 | per 1000 | | |
| | 5500 | 450 | | | |
| | 69 | 99 | % | | |
| access to safe water | 71 | 97 | % | low | high |
| | 62 | 74 | years | | |

## The 27 EU countries

**3** How are these EU programmes attempting to narrow the gaps?

European Regional Development Fund ................................................................

........................................................................................................................................

European Social Fund ................................................................

........................................................................................................................................

European Cohesion Fund ................................................................

........................................................................................................................................

**(3 marks)**

# The world divided into developed and developing

**10 mins**

**1 (a)** Name the continents which contain

    **(i)** mostly developed countries

    ....................................................

    ....................................................

    ....................................................

    **(ii)** mostly developing countries.

    ....................................................

    ....................................................

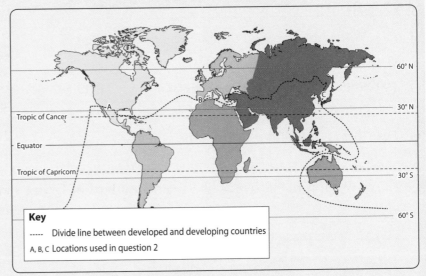

**Key**

----- Divide line between developed and developing countries

A, B, C Locations used in question 2

**(b)** Describe the course of the divide line between developed and developing countries referring to

    **(i)** main direction followed .................................................................................

    **(ii)** where it changes direction .............................................................................

    **(iii)** latitude ....................................................................................................

**2** The table below shows measures of development for selected countries in 2005–6.

| | | GNI per head ($US) | Birth rate (per 1000) | Life expectancy (years) | People per doctor | Access to safe water (%) |
|---|---|---|---|---|---|---|
| **A** | USA | 44,710 | 14 | 78 | 435 | 100 |
| | Mexico | 7,100 | 22 | 76 | 1900 | 91 |
| **B** | Spain | 27,800 | 9 | 80 | 410 | 98 |
| | Morocco | 1,770 | 23 | 71 | 2000 | 80 |
| **C** | Japan | 39,630 | 9 | 82 | 476 | 100 |
| | Russia | 4,560 | 9 | 65 | 290 | 96 |
| | South Korea | 17,690 | 9 | 78 | 455 | 92 |
| | China | 2,000 | 12 | 72 | 667 | 77 |

**(a)** How strongly do these development values support the course of the divide line between developed and developing countries at map locations A, B and C? Mark X on each of the three strength lines to show how strongly you feel they support the course of the line.

Weak     **A**     Strong    Weak     **B**     Strong   Weak     **C**     Strong

    strength line          strength line          strength line

**(b)** Briefly explain the position of your X for either A or B, and for C.

    A or B ...............................................................................................................

    ..........................................................................................................................

    C .......................................................................................................................

    ..........................................................................................................................

UNDERSTANDING GCSE GEOGRAPHY

# Global inequalities

**1** Use words from the box to fill in the gaps below. One of them is used twice; all the others are used only once.

| | | | | | |
|---|---|---|---|---|---|
| developed | developing | drought | earthquakes | floods | physical |
| political | social | tropical storms | unfair world trade | wealth gap | |

'Global inequalities in income and development' refers to the ............................... between rich ............................... countries and poor ............................... countries. These are exacerbated (made worse) by both physical and human factors. Natural hazards are examples of a ............................... factor. The four natural hazards which kill most people worldwide are ..............................., ..............................., ..............................., and ............................... . Of these, the one which hits poor countries more of the time, because so many are located in low latitudes, is ............................... . The main economic factor is ............................... . Differences in the availability of, and people's access to, safe water is an example of a ............................... factor. The impact of unstable and corrupt governments is a ............................... factor.

**2 (a)** Poor preparation is one reason why the impact of natural hazards is greater in poor countries, widening global inequalities. Write in the natural hazards for which the preparations named are most useful.

| Ways to prepare for natural hazards | Natural hazard(s) |
|---|---|
| build shelters stocked with emergency supplies of food and drinking water | |
| government controlled stores of staple foodstuffs | |
| trained emergency rescue services | |
| strong well-constructed buildings using high grade materials | |
| medical teams with field hospitals | |
| stores of tents, blankets and chemical toilets | |
| improved weather forecasts, regularly updated on radio and TV | |

**(b)** Explain why poor countries are less prepared for natural hazards, and why more people die than in rich countries.

......................................................................................................................................................

......................................................................................................................................................

......................................................................................................................................................

# World trade and aid

10 mins

## Unfair trade

1 (a) Complete the percentage income ratio for coffee:
developing countries ..........:.......... developed countries

(b) How does it show unfair world trade?

.............................................................................................

.............................................................................................

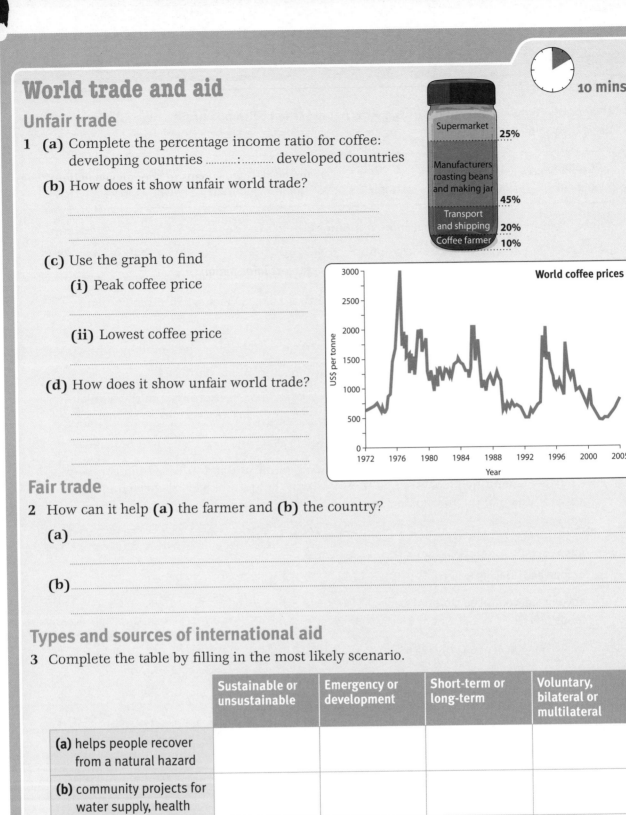

Supermarket 25%

Manufacturers roasting beans and making jar 45%

Transport and shipping 20%

Coffee farmer 10%

(c) Use the graph to find

(i) Peak coffee price

.............................................................................................

(ii) Lowest coffee price

.............................................................................................

(d) How does it show unfair world trade?

.............................................................................................

.............................................................................................

.............................................................................................

**World coffee prices**

US$ per tonne — Year 1972 to 2005

## Fair trade

2 How can it help (a) the farmer and (b) the country?

(a) .............................................................................................

.............................................................................................

(b) .............................................................................................

.............................................................................................

## Types and sources of international aid

3 Complete the table by filling in the most likely scenario.

| | Sustainable or unsustainable | Emergency or development | Short-term or long-term | Voluntary, bilateral or multilateral |
|---|---|---|---|---|
| (a) helps people recover from a natural hazard | | | | |
| (b) community projects for water supply, health | | | | |
| (c) large-scale projects such as large dams, new roads | | | | |

(d) Give two advantages and disadvantages of aid for countries receiving the aid (recipients).

| Advantages | Disadvantages |
|---|---|
| 1 .................................... | 1 .................................... |
| .................................... | .................................... |
| 2 .................................... | 2 .................................... |
| .................................... | .................................... |

## DEVELOPING WORLD – ONE NATURAL HAZARD

Possibilities:
tectonic – earthquake, volcano (ch 1)
climatic – tropical storm (ch 3), flooding (ch 5)

**Name and location** .........................................................

.........................................................................................

**Causes** .......................................................................

.........................................................................................

.........................................................................................

**Impact** .......................................................................

.........................................................................................

.........................................................................................

**Responses** .................................................................

.........................................................................................

**Assessment:** why poor countries are affected worse than rich countries .......................................

.........................................................................................

.........................................................................................

.........................................................................................

## DEVELOPING WORLD – ONE DEVELOPMENT PROJECT

Possibilities:
financial – credit/loans to poor for self improvement
charity/NGO aid – for local/small-scale projects

**Name and location** .........................................................

.........................................................................................

**Project information** ......................................................

.........................................................................................

.........................................................................................

.........................................................................................

**Changes** .....................................................................

.........................................................................................

.........................................................................................

**Assessment:** results and levels of success .............

.........................................................................................

.........................................................................................

.........................................................................................

## TWO CONTRASTING EU COUNTRIES FOR LEVEL OF DEVELOPMENT

### 1 WEALTHY COUNTRY

**Name and location within EU** ...........................................

.........................................................................................

**Measures showing high development** .............................

.........................................................................................

.........................................................................................

.........................................................................................

**Causes** .......................................................................

.........................................................................................

.........................................................................................

.........................................................................................

### 2 LESS WEALTHY COUNTRY

**Name and location within EU** ...........................................

.........................................................................................

**Measures showing lower development** ...........................

.........................................................................................

.........................................................................................

.........................................................................................

**Causes** .......................................................................

.........................................................................................

.........................................................................................

.........................................................................................

**List of EU ways to reduce inequalities in development**

.........................................................................................

.........................................................................................

.........................................................................................

.........................................................................................

.........................................................................................

## PRACTICE GCSE QUESTIONS

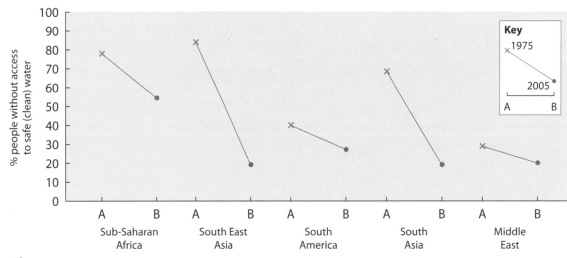

**Figure 1**

## Question 1

**Figure 1** gives information about people's access to clean (safe) water in five regions of the developing world in 1975 and 2005. From Figure 1, name the world region in which

**(a)** the greatest percentage of people had access to safe water in 1975

**(b)** the greatest percentage of people were without access to safe water in 2005

**(c)** there was the largest percentage improvement of people with access to safe water between 1975 and 2005

**(d)** there was the least improvement in the percentage with access to safe water between 1975 and 2005.

**(4 marks)**

Read the student's answer to question 1. Then, before you mark their answers and give your comments on them, listen to some advice from the examiner on the type of graph shown in Figure 1 and what it shows.

### Student's answer

| | |
|---|---|
| (a) South East Asia | |
| (b) Sub-Saharan Africa | |
| (c) South Asia | |
| (d) Middle East | |

### Your verdict

✔ or ✘    Comment

☐  .............................................

☐  .............................................

☐  .............................................

☐  .............................................

## Question 2

Describe how both physical and human factors need to be studied to explain the widening gap in wealth between the world's rich and poor countries.    **(6 marks)**

## Student's answer

> the physical factor is natural hazards, which affect poor countries worse than rich countries. Examples of natural hazards are tropical storms, floods and earthquakes. Poor countries are not prepared and have many poorly-built houses in shanty towns
>
> - the human factors include unfair world trade and people stuck in the poverty trap
>
> - fair trade gives farmers in developing countries higher prices for their crops, but farmers still get a low price. Only about 10% of what we pay for a banana goes to the farmer in the Caribbean who grows it.
>
> - people in poor countries have a lower quality of life than those in rich countries. A big problem for many of them is access to clean water. Without this, diseases are common, people cannot work as well, farm output goes down, there is less food to eat and poor people get stuck in the poverty trap.
>
> - governments are bad. Look at the Mugabe government in Zimbabwe.

## Examiner's verdict

- Has the student identified factors? ✔
- Do the factors include both physical and human? ✔
- Are all the factors relevant to the theme of the question? ✔
- Has the student described more fully to explain why the poor remain poor? ✔
- Is more precise but relevant information relating to examples included? ✔
- Has the student made best use of their knowledge and understanding with good organisational skills and some comment about widening gap between rich and poor? ✗

**Overall**, this answer reaches the top of Level 2, which makes it worth 4 marks. Grade B standard. In one way it is an organised answer; the student goes through the factors, both physical and human, in a systematic way. What holds it back is its layout. Dashes give the same impression as bullet points; they make an answer look note-like. It is not so easy to add comment about 'both physical and human factors need to be studied' or 'the widening gap in wealth'.

## Do better

Write your own top Level 3 answer worth 6 marks on a separate piece of lined paper. Take advantage of the strong points in this student's answer and improve on the weak points.

6 mins

**HOW WELL DID YOU DO? SEE PAGE 119**

# Globalisation

## Summary

Faster communications between people and countries means that the world has become a smaller place. Most big companies now operate globally, with factories and offices in many different countries. Industrial growth has spread to the developing world, and to China in particular. Population and economic growth are causing an increase in the global demand for energy. Resulting concerns about pollution and unsustainable development are encouraging the search for alternative renewable energy sources. The need to satisfy increasing global demand for food is also raising concerns about long-term sustainability.

## Checklists for revision

| KEY IDEAS | Understand and know | Need more revision |
|---|---|---|
| **Globalisation is a significant feature of the world in the 21st century** | | |
| I understand what globalisation means. | | |
| **Globalisation has led to the growth manufacturing industry and services across the world** | | |
| I can describe the main characteristics of TNCs and give an example. | | |
| I can describe the developments in communications which allow big companies to operate globally. | | |
| **The relative importance of manufacturing to different countries is changing, some declining and others growing** | | |
| I can explain why some companies have moved factories from the UK to Asia. | | |
| I know why China has become the world's new manufacturing giant. | | |
| **Impacts of increasing global energy use are encouraging the search for less polluting and more sustainable renewable sources** | | |
| I am able to explain the environmental disadvantages of using fossil fuels. | | |
| I can give some of the advantages and disadvantages of using renewable sources of energy. | | |
| **The global search to satisfy increasing demands for food is having repercussions on the environment and people that are more negative than positive** | | |
| I can describe some of the environmental damage being caused by increasing global demand for food. | | |
| I can explain some of the economic and social issues resulting from subsistence farmers changing to growing cash crops. | | |

| CASE STUDIES – can you name an example and write about it? | | |
|---|---|---|
| **One TNC** – location of HQ, other locations around the world, types of businesses | | |
| **China's development into an economic giant** – world importance, types of industry, reasons for growth | | |
| **One type of renewable energy** – how it works, where it is generated, its advantages and disadvantages | | |

# A quick guide to globalisation and its consequences

 **10 mins**

1  Globalisation is: increasing importance of international operations for people and companies. How did each of these factors make globalisation possible?

  **(a)** The telecommunications revolution ........................................................................

  ............................................................................................................................ **(3 marks)**

  **(b)** The jet aircraft ..................................................................................... **(2 marks)**

  **(c)** Container ships ..................................................................................... **(2 marks)**

2  Global interdependence is shared need between countries for one another's goods or services.

> **Types of goods and services shared and exchanged between countries**
>
> | | |
> |---|---|
> | raw materials (e.g. hardwoods, natural rubber) | knowledge of modern technology |
> | low-priced manufactured goods | people seeking hot/different holiday destinations |
> | high-tech manufactured goods | skilled workers (e.g. engineers, teachers) |
> | tropical foodstuffs | varied environments for tourism (e.g. big game, warm seas) |
>
> **Key:** ☐ income sources for rich countries   ☐ income sources for poor countries

  **(a)** Colour or shade the types of goods and services in the box above, according to whether they are more likely to be income sources for rich or poor countries. Complete the key.

  **(4 marks)**

  **(b)** Explain how interdependence between countries is shown.

  ............................................................................................................................

  ............................................................................................................................ **(2 marks)**

3  What are TNCs?

  ............................................................................................................................ **(2 marks)**

Locations of the head offices of the world's top 100 biggest companies in 2009

4  **(a)** Shade or colour countries inside the bar according to whether they are developed or developing, and complete the key. **(2 marks)**

  **(b)** What is:

  **(i)** USA percentage ........................   **(ii)** China percentage ........................

  **(iii)** Ratio between developed and developing worlds ........................ **(2 marks)**

5  Country labels after globalisation. Name the countries called the

  **(a)** Factory of the world ...........................................................................

  **(b)** Buyer of the world .............................................................................

  **(c)** IT office to the world (for support services) ........................................ **(3 marks)**

# Changing world: de-industrialisation and industrial growth

## De-industrialisation in the UK

**1** Percentages of total GDP in the UK from manufacturing industry.

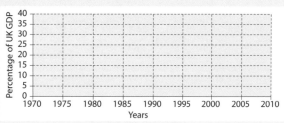

**Manufacturing as percentage of UK GDP:**

| 1970: 32 | 1975: 28 | 1980: 26 | 1985: 24 | 1990: 22 |
|---|---|---|---|---|
| 1995: 21 | 2000: 18 | 2005: 14 | 2010: 13 | |

**(a)** Plot these percentages as a line graph.

**(b)** How do they show de-industrialisation?

**2** Percentage of components sourced in UK by the UK company making JCBs (yellow diggers).

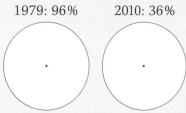

1979: 96%          2010: 36%

**(a)** Show the percentages in the two pie graphs.

**(b)** How do they indicate the effects of globalisation?

**3** Number of steel workers on Teesside.

| Year | 1914 | 1960s | 2000 | 2010 |
|---|---|---|---|---|
| No of workers | 45,000 | 16,000 | 3,000 | 0 |

Explain how these factors have affected the number of steel workers on Teesside.

**(a)** improved technology

**(b)** de-industrialisation

**(c)** globalisation

## Industrial growth in China

**4** The world's five largest manufacturers in 2009 (US$ billions output).

| North America | Europe | Asia |
|---|---|---|
| USA 1830 | Germany 670 | China 1050 |
| | UK 350 | Japan 930 |

**(a)** What is China's world ranking?

**(b)** How many times greater is industrial output in China than in the UK?

**(c)** How is China different from all the other four?

**5** Exports of China (2008).

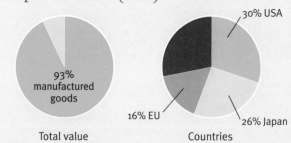

30% USA

93% manufactured goods

16% EU          26% Japan

Total value          Countries

China dominates world exports of computers, phones, electrical goods, clothing, trainers and toys.

**5** What are the differences between China and the UK in terms of:

**(a)** importance of manufacturing industry

**(b)** types of goods made and exported.

**6** Describe four factors for growth of industry in China.

1 ........................................................

2 ........................................................

3 ........................................................

4 ........................................................

# Increasing global energy demand – how sustainable is it?

## Main causes of increasing global energy demand

### A Population growth

**1 (a)** Use Figure 1 on page 70 to fill in the world total population figures below.

| Year | World population (billions) |
|---|---|
| 1830 | |
| 1960 | |
| 1999 | |
| 2050 (predicted) | |

**(b)** List reasons why population growth increases energy demand.

### B Growing economic development in Asia

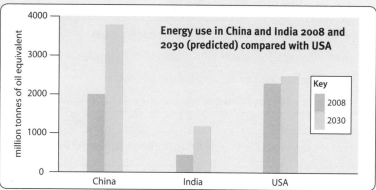

**(c)** How is the **rate** of predicted increase in energy use in China and India by 2030 different from the USA?

**(d)** How and why is it related to further economic development in Asia?

## The world still relies heavily on fossil fuels

**2**

World energy use by source 2008

Other renewables
Nuclear
HEP
Biomass & waste
Oil
Coal
Gas

Key
☐ fossil fuels
☐ renewables
☐ other

**(a)** On the pie chart, shade in energy sources according to whether they are fossil fuels, renewables or neither of these. Complete the key.

**(b)** What is the approximate percentage of total world energy use from fossil fuels?

**(c)** List **three** reasons why it is so high.

1
2
3

**(d)** List examples of consequences of fossil fuel use on these environments

**(i)** Land

**(ii)** Water

**(iii)** Air

## Replacement of fossil fuels by renewables

**3 (a)** Why has increased use of renewables such as wind in the UK been slow?

**(b)** Why might their use speed up now and in the future?

# Issues arising from global demands for more food

 10 mins

1 State the main reason for increasing global food demands.

.................................................................................................................................

2 The five big issues are named in the table below. Complete the table by following the instructions in the boxes below.

---

**Causes – assign the correct cause to each issue**

- need for irrigation water which is in short supply
- importing food long distances from overseas
- money needed for fertilisers, pesticides, irrigation water
- over use of marginal farmland
- more money made growing crops for sale

▼

**Negative repercussions – distribute these to the relevant issue (two for each one)**

- hard to pay back borrowed money in bad years
- flash points such as Nile Basin water
- indigenous farmers driven off land
- potential for hostilities between countries
- CO₂ emissions and global warming
- increased soil erosion
- larger carbon footprint
- own food supply no longer grown
- loss of soil fertility
- rural poverty trap worsens

▼

**Factor – write down whether each issue is an** economic, environmental, political or social factor ▶ **Further details – fill in any relevant further details** such as positive repercussions, ways to tackle issue, named examples

---

| | ISSUES | | | | |
| --- | --- | --- | --- | --- | --- |
| | **Food miles** | **Environmental degradation** | **Water wars** | **Subsistence replaced by cash crop** | **Rural debt** |
| **Cause** | | | | | |
| **Negative repercussions** | | | | | |
| **Factor** | | | | | |
| **Further details** | | | | | |

## ONE TNC

Company .............................................................

**Location of HQ** .............................................................

**Location of other world operations** .............................................................
.............................................................
.............................................................
.............................................................

**Types of businesses** .............................................................
.............................................................
.............................................................
.............................................................
.............................................................
.............................................................
.............................................................

## ONE TYPE OF RENEWABLE ENERGY

Type .............................................................

**How it works; types of location needed** .............................................................
.............................................................
.............................................................
.............................................................

**Named examples of locations** .............................................................
.............................................................

**Advantages** .............................................................
.............................................................
.............................................................

**Disadvantages** .............................................................
.............................................................
.............................................................

## DEVELOPMENT OF CHINA AS THE WORLD'S NEW ECONOMIC GIANT

**World importance for manufacturing industry**
.............................................................
.............................................................
.............................................................

**Types of industry**
.............................................................
.............................................................
.............................................................
.............................................................
.............................................................

**Main industrial locations**
.............................................................
.............................................................
.............................................................

**Reasons for industrial growth**
.............................................................
.............................................................
.............................................................
.............................................................
.............................................................
.............................................................
.............................................................

**Current and future prospects**
.............................................................
.............................................................
.............................................................
.............................................................
.............................................................

## PRACTICE GCSE QUESTIONS

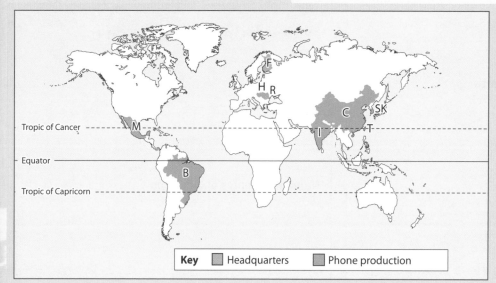

| Country | Production (million phones) |
|---|---|
| Finland | 85 |
| Romania | 35 |
| Hungary | 40 |
| India | 25 |
| China | 165 |
| South Korea | 15 |
| Taiwan | 10 |
| Brazil | 40 |
| Mexico | 20 |

**Key**  ▢ Headquarters  ▢ Phone production

**Figure 1**

## Question 1

**Figure 1** shows where Nokia mobile phones are produced and how many. Describe the world distribution of Nokia mobile phone production.

**(3 marks)**

## Student's answer

Nokia's headquarters is in Europe in Finland which makes the 2nd highest number of mobiles of any country. Top country for making Nokia phones is China, with 165 million, twice as many as Finland. Phones are made in three other Asian countries (South Korea, Taiwan and India), but in much smaller numbers. A lot of phones are made in Europe, still not quite as many as in China. No Nokia phones are made in Africa, Australia or America.

## Examiner's verdict

A full mark answer – what is good about it?

• All the time is spent on describing the distribution shown on the map; no space is wasted.

• Phone production numbers are used to show how some countries are more important than others.

• The student looks at the distribution in relation to continents, not just named countries.

• The student also refers to continents and places without Nokia phone production. When describing a world distribution, doing this is good practice because it improves the global view.

Any quibbles? Only the loose use of 'America'. Hopefully the student meant USA rather than all of North America, because Mexico is considered part of the continent of North America.

Look at the mark scheme used for question 1.

## Mark scheme for question 1

Phone production in four continents (Europe, Asia, North and South America)

Most output in Asia 215m

Second highest in Europe 160m

Production absent from Africa and Australasia

China the country with most production/almost double that of Finland

Headquarters in Finland in Europe with the second highest production

Production in Brazil double that of Mexico in Latin America

**Three points along these lines describing world distribution. 3 @ 1 mark = 3 marks**

Which **three** points in the mark scheme were definitely included in the student's answer?

.......................................................................................................................................................

.......................................................................................................................................................

.......................................................................................................................................................

## Question 2

Explain why TNCs (such as Nokia) favour some countries of the world for locating their production more than others. **(6 marks)**

## Student's answer

> The main reason why big companies are moving factories from the UK to the Far East is cheap labour. Wages rates are only 20% of those in the UK and goods can be made much cheaper despite the costs of shipping them to the UK. Living costs are lower and Asian workers seem willing to work long hours, six days a week, in terrible conditions. They are just pleased to have a job that is much better paid than other jobs like farming. China is the main choice for many TNCs because costs are lowest there. Also many think it is going to get better in China. A big country, growing home market. A great future.

## Examiner's verdict

So far, so good... but this is only a part-answer. When a student doesn't fill all the lines left for answering, it doesn't automatically mean that the answer is inadequate – just as it doesn't follow that when a student has filled all the lines a full mark answer has been written. However, what it usually means is that the answer falls short of what is needed for the number of marks, as here.

Which part of the question set has not been addressed?

The question is about TNCs favouring some countries more than others. So far this student has only referred to favoured countries and some of their attractions.

**Overall**, this answer reaches Level 2 and is worth about half marks. Grade C standard. The message? Answer all parts of the question set. Only then do you stand a chance of claiming all the marks.

## Do better

Finish off the student's answer and turn it into a top Level 3 answer worth 6 marks. Make maximum use of the space left for answering that the student didn't use.

**5 mins**

**HOW WELL DID YOU DO? SEE PAGE 119**

# Tourism

## Summary

The global growth of tourism has been dramatic. Different natural environments, such as mountains and coasts, have tourist potential, as do many big cities. Tourism is a business; it needs good management to maintain income levels. Mass tourism helps economic development for both regions and countries, but it is not without negative effects. The market for adventure holidays is increasing as tourists seek out extreme environments. Long-term management and ecotourism developments are needed to reduce the increasing environmental risks from tourism growth.

## Checklists for revision

| KEY IDEAS | Understand and know | Need more revision |
|---|---|---|
| **Global growth of tourism has led to the exploitation of a range of different environments** | | |
| I know reasons why global tourism has grown so fast. | | |
| I can name examples of coastal areas, mountains and cities visited by many tourists and describe their attractions. | | |
| **Effective management strategies are needed for the continued prosperity of the UK's tourist areas** | | |
| I can give examples of places where tourism is an important industry in the UK and explain why. | | |
| I can describe measures from UK Authorities in either coastal resorts or National Parks to try to ensure successful tourism. | | |
| **Mass tourism brings many advantages, but strategies need to be in place to limit long-term damage** | | |
| I understand what is meant by mass tourism and can name examples of mass tourism areas. | | |
| I know positive and negative effects of mass tourism for both the economies of countries and the environment. | | |
| I can describe ways to reduce these negative impacts. | | |
| **Extreme environments have a high risk of environmental damage from the growth of tourism** | | |
| I can give examples of extreme environments which are attracting more adventurous tourists and describe their attractions. | | |
| I am able to explain why these are fragile environments at high risk from the impact of tourism. | | |
| **The development of ecotourism will help tourism to become a sustainable industry**<br>I can describe ways in which ecotourism is different from other types of tourism. | | |

| CASE STUDIES – can you name an example and write about it? | | |
|---|---|---|
| **Coastal resort or National Park in the UK** – reasons for growth, visitor strategies, their effectiveness and plans for the future | | |
| **Tropical tourist area** – attractions, benefits and problems, strategies and plans | | |
| **Extreme environment** – attractions, tourism impacts, measures in place, coping in the future | | |
| **Ecotourism** – characteristics, benefits, sustainable development | | |

# Tourism and travel quiz

**10 mins**

1 Cities have many different attractions for tourists. Use the lists to match each city with its country and its visitor attractions. Add details of your own for London. **(9 marks)**

| Countries: | Australia | Brazil | France | Greece | Italy | Saudi Arabia | USA |
|---|---|---|---|---|---|---|---|

**Tourist attractions:** Parthenon & Acropolis     Times Square & Statue of Liberty
Canals & St Mark's Square     Carnival & Statue of Christ     Colosseum & Vatican City
Eiffel Tower & Louvre     Holy Kaaba & Haj pilgrimage     Opera House & Harbour Bridge

**(a) Athens**       **(b) London**       **(c) Mecca**

Country ......................................

Tourist attractions ......................................

**(d) New York**       **(e) Paris**       **(f) Rio de Janeiro**

Country ......................................

Tourist attractions ......................................

**(g) Rome**       **(h) Sydney**       **(i) Venice**

Country ......................................

Tourist attractions ......................................

2 Different environments and places offer different attractions for UK holidaymakers.

**List of locations:** Amazon jungle lodge     Antarctica     Antigua and Barbados     Nepal trekking
Benidorm and Majorca     Blackpool and Brighton     Egypt's Red Sea resorts
English Lake District     Italian lakes (e.g. Lake Garda)     Kenya tented safari camp

From the list, choose two examples for each holiday type; however, for one you will need to name your own two examples. **(7 marks)**

**Mass tourism**

summer: beach     summer: mountain scenery     winter: beach       winter: ski

...................... ...................... ...................... ......................

...................... ......................

**Adventure and ecotourism**

adventure holidays ......................     ecotourism ......................

......................

3 The top 10 most visited long-haul country destinations from the UK are: **1** USA, **2** India, **3** Canada, **4** Australia, **5** UAE (mainly Dubai), **6** Egypt, **7** China, **8** South Africa, **9** Pakistan, **10** Thailand

From the list, choose the country which best fits each of these descriptions. **(4 marks)**

**(a)** Desert country which now has the world's tallest building ......................

**(b)** Visited by relatives and friends only, not ordinary tourists ......................

**(c)** The theme parks are big attractions for many UK family holidays ......................

**(d)** Most tourists visit the pyramids at Giza and take a Nile cruise ......................

# Global growth of tourism and climatic influences on tourist areas

10 mins

**World tourist numbers 1950–2010**

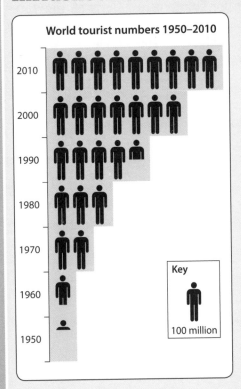

**Key**

👤 100 million

## Global tourism growth

**1(a)(i)** World tourist numbers were 25 million in 1950. By how many times had they increased by 2010?

..........................................................................

..........................................................................

**(ii)** What happened to world tourist numbers between these years? (One word answers are acceptable.)

1980 and 2010 ........................................

1990 and 2010 ........................................

**(b)** Three main factors for the growth of global tourism are stated below. Briefly explain the importance of each one.

**(i)** greater wealth ..............................................

..........................................................................

**(ii)** more leisure time ...........................................

..........................................................................

**(iii)** improved transport .......................................

## Climatic influences on environments for tourism

**Average monthly temperatures and rainfall**

| **Barbados** in the Caribbean | J | F | M | A | M | J | J | A | S | O | N | D |
|---|---|---|---|---|---|---|---|---|---|---|---|---|
| Temperature (°C) | 25 | 25 | 25 | 26 | 27 | 27 | 27 | 27 | 27 | 27 | 26 | 25 |
| Precipitation (mm) | 66 | 28 | 33 | 36 | 58 | 112 | 147 | 147 | 170 | 178 | 206 | 97 |
| **Costa del Sol** in Spain | J | F | M | A | M | J | J | A | S | O | N | D |
| Temperature (°C) | 12 | 12 | 15 | 17 | 19 | 22 | 25 | 26 | 24 | 20 | 16 | 13 |
| Precipitation (mm) | 31 | 21 | 21 | 28 | 18 | 4 | 0 | 6 | 16 | 25 | 27 | 36 |
| **Swiss Alps** at 2500 metres | J | F | M | A | M | J | J | A | S | O | N | D |
| Temperature (°C) | -9 | -9 | -6 | -4 | +1 | +3 | +5 | +5 | +3 | 0 | -5 | -8 |
| Precipitation (mm) | 202 | 180 | 164 | 166 | 197 | 249 | 302 | 278 | 209 | 183 | 190 | 169 |

**Key**
■ peak tourist season
□ wet season

**2 (a)** Shade or colour precipitation values to highlight the wet season in each place. Complete the key.

**(b)** Describe how climate helps to explain when the time of the peak season is in each place.

**(i)** Caribbean ................................................

..........................................................................

**(ii)** Spain ......................................................

..........................................................................

**(iii)** High in the Alps .......................................

..........................................................................

# Economic benefits of tourism – label and complete

10 mins

## Multiplier effect of tourism for jobs and economic growth

1 Label the branches of the tourist tree to show how the growth of tourism can have a multiplier effect on services, industries, jobs and income. Some of the knock-on effects of tourism in infrastructure and public services have been filled in to get you started.

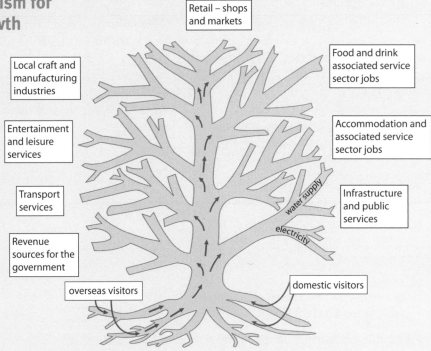

Retail – shops and markets

Local craft and manufacturing industries

Food and drink associated service sector jobs

Entertainment and leisure services

Accommodation and associated service sector jobs

Transport services

water supply

Infrastructure and public services

Revenue sources for the government

electricity

overseas visitors

domestic visitors

## Multiplier effect of tourism for the local area and national economy

2 Fill in the boxes in the two flow diagrams. Choose from the list below and place in the best order.

| List | Local area — More jobs both formal and informal | National economy — Country earns more foreign exchange |
|---|---|---|
| Better educated, more skilled workers | | |
| Can afford to buy expertise and goods from overseas | | |
| Living standards improve for all, not just tourism workers | | |
| More money spent in markets, shops and on local services | | |
| New airports, roads, luxury hotels built | | |
| People can pay to improve homes and have their children educated | | |
| Purchasing power of local people increases | | |
| Tourist infrastructure and facilities are modernised | | |
| Wealthier tourists with high spending power attracted | | |

# Negative effects of tourism and strategies for management

10 mins

## Negative effects of tourism

**1** The negative effects described in the table below refer to different types of holidays, such as **summer coastal**, **winter ski**, **holidays in extreme environments** and **tropical tourism in developing countries**. Fill in the table.

| Negative effect | Is it mainly economic, environmental or social? | Type of holiday and named example of area |
|---|---|---|
| **(a)** Wild animals disturbed by armies of tourist minibuses, also destroying vegetation in the dry season. | | |
| **(b)** Spiral of decline from persistent drop in tourist numbers over many years. | | |
| **(c)** Orchards and vineyards replaced by concrete jungles of hotels, villas, roads and airports. | | |
| **(d)** Indigenous tribes and groups of people driven off their traditional land to make way for tourism facilities. | | |
| **(e)** Remote sparsely populated fragile environments put at risk of litter, air and water pollution by visitors. | | |
| **(f)** A study of vegetation found 9% less plant cover and 11% fewer plant species on the most used mountain slopes. | | |

## Strategies for management towards more sustainable tourism

**2** Give more information about the two examples below.

| NATIONAL or WILDLIFE PARKS | ECOTOURISM AND RESPONSIBLE TOURISM |
|---|---|
| **Definition** ................................................. | **Definition** ................................................. |
| .......................................................................... | .......................................................................... |
| **Purposes** – how they are met | **Purposes** – how they are met |
| (a) Conservation ........................................... | (a) Environmental ........................................ |
| .......................................................................... | .......................................................................... |
| (b) Access for tourists ................................ | (b) for Local people .................................... |
| .......................................................................... | .......................................................................... |
| **Types of areas** ......................................... | **Types of areas** ......................................... |
| .......................................................................... | .......................................................................... |
| Examples ....................................................... | Examples ....................................................... |
| .......................................................................... | .......................................................................... |
| **Why not more widely used?** ................... | **Why not more widely used?** ................... |
| .......................................................................... | .......................................................................... |

# Know your case studies: key facts

## UK NATIONAL PARK OR COASTAL RESORT

Name ........................................................................

**Reasons for growth/attractions**

........................................................................

........................................................................

........................................................................

**Management strategies for visitors**

........................................................................

........................................................................

........................................................................

**Effectiveness of strategies**

........................................................................

........................................................................

........................................................................

**Plans for the future**

........................................................................

........................................................................

........................................................................

## TROPICAL TOURIST AREA

Name ........................................................................

**Reasons for growth/attractions**

........................................................................

........................................................................

........................................................................

**Positive effects (benefits)**

........................................................................

........................................................................

........................................................................

**Negative effects (costs)**

........................................................................

........................................................................

........................................................................

**Strategies and plans for the future**

........................................................................

........................................................................

........................................................................

## EXTREME ENVIRONMENT

Name ........................................................................

**Attractions**

........................................................................

........................................................................

........................................................................

**Impact of tourism**

........................................................................

........................................................................

**Measures in place**

........................................................................

........................................................................

........................................................................

**Can it cope with tourist development?**

........................................................................

## ECOTOURISM

Name ........................................................................

**Characteristics**

........................................................................

........................................................................

**Benefits**

Environment ........................................................................

Local economy ........................................................................

Lives of the people ........................................................................

**How it contributes to sustainable development**

........................................................................

........................................................................

# GradeStudio

## GCSE QUESTIONS AND TWO STUDENTS' ANSWERS

### Question 1

Study the photograph of Benidorm located on the Mediterranean coast of Spain. This is an example of mass summer tourism. Describe the photographic evidence for this. **(3 marks)**

## Student's answer

Mass tourism means lots of tourists going there, tourism on a big scale.[1]

The time of mass tourism began with the coming of package holidays with everything from air travel to hotels arranged in advance.[2]

The photo shows the beach in Benidorm absolutely packed and crowded with sun bathers and people standing in the warm waters.[3]

## Examiner's verdict

1 A brief definition of mass tourism has not been asked for.

2 Background information about the rise of mass tourism is definitely not needed.

3 Here there is some description from the photograph, relevant to the question set. However, there is not enough elaboration or comment on mass tourism for it to be worth more than 1 mark.

**Overall**, 1 out of the 3 marks. Too much background information about mass tourism, and not enough description and use of photographic evidence. What else on the photo shows that this is an example of mass summer tourism? Many students believe that they have given full answers when they have filled all the lines! Are you one of them? If a student is going to write as little as this, everything written must be relevant to the question to have any hope of full marks.

## Do better

Write a top Level 2 answer worth 4 marks.

**3 mins**

## Question 2

For either a National Park or a coastal resort in the UK, describe the management plans and strategies to ensure tourism success in the area. **(6 marks)**

### Student's answer

One National Park is the Lake District. The NPA looks after its management. There are strict controls in National Parks about new buildings. Regulations also apply to repairing and renovating old properties to make sure that local building materials are used and that they blend in. One big problem is footpath erosion from so many walkers. The NPA in the Lake District manages this by repairing surfaces with stone slabs and steps or changing the route in the most badly eroded places. By providing and improving tourist facilities like picnic sites, car parks and toilets, other areas are saved from damage.

One coastal resort is Blackpool. Its main problem is the opposite of the Lake District's. Numbers of visitors keep going down and tourist places are going out of business. The Local Authority has made big efforts since 2001 to smarten up the place, clearing old buildings and cleaning up the beach to Blue Flag levels. The big push was to fund new attractions like Water World and casinos, as well as improve old ones like the Pleasure Beach.

### Examiner's verdict

This student has given answers for **both** a National Park and a coastal resort. Crazy, but you would be surprised how many students do this in GCSE exams in questions with a choice, as here. Some students might even do it deliberately hoping that the examiner will mark all of both answers and give them a higher mark!

Is the student ever going to be able to write enough about one of them for Level 3 in the time and space available? Unlikely. And what happens if the policy is to mark only the first one (National Park) and ignore the second (coastal resort)? Which is the better part of this student's answer, or are the answers for National Park and coastal resort both worth the same? What do you think?

**Overall**, however the examiner marks it, this is a Level 2 answer, essentially grade C standard. The merit in both answers is that an appropriate example is named, and the focus throughout is kept on management plans and strategies. The coastal resort answer, although shorter, is slightly better because more details specific to Blackpool are included.

### Do better

On a separate sheet of lined paper improve this answer and write a top Level 3 answer worth 6 marks, either by expanding on one of the same examples, or by using another example of your own choice. For a 6 mark answer like this, you will usually be given 12 lines on which to write your answer.

**6 mins**

**HOW WELL DID YOU DO? SEE PAGE 119**

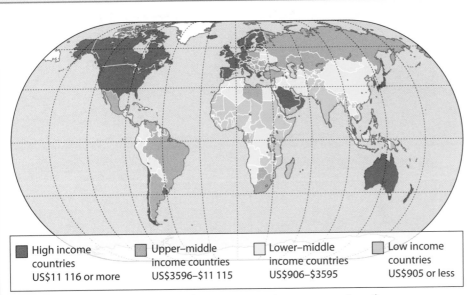

**Figure 1** GNI per capita, 2006 (Gross National Income per head)

Key:
- High income countries US$11 116 or more
- Upper–middle income countries US$3596–$11 115
- Lower–middle income countries US$906–$3595
- Low income countries US$905 or less

**Typical GCSE questions**

1 Describe the global distribution of countries according to levels of income.

2 Describe the world pattern of countries with higher and lower than average incomes.

3 Describe what the map shows about world variations in countries' incomes.

4 Describe how the map shows great global variations in wealth.

The map in **Figure 1** gives a general view of the great inequalities in wealth between different parts of the world. The questions are included to give you an idea of the sort of questions you might be asked. Now move on to practise answering some questions.

# USEFUL KNOWLEDGE FOR DESCRIBING GLOBAL DISTRIBUTIONS AND PATTERNS

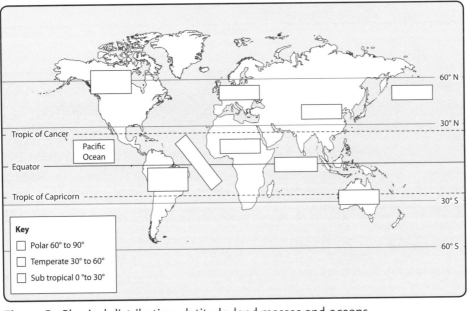

**Figure 2** Physical distribution– latitude, land masses and oceans

Key
- ☐ Polar 60° to 90°
- ☐ Temperate 30° to 60°
- ☐ Sub tropical 0 °to 30°

## Questions

1 On the map in **Figure 2**

**(a)** shade in the extent of the three world zones and complete the key

**(b)** name in the boxes the six inhabited continents

**(c)** name the main oceans in the remaining three boxes

**(d)** label Northern Hemisphere and Southern Hemisphere.

2 Study **Figures 1 and 2**. Fill in the table below according to whether the six continents contain mainly high or low income countries.

| Mainly high incomes | Mainly low incomes |
| --- | --- |
|  |  |
|  |  |
|  |  |

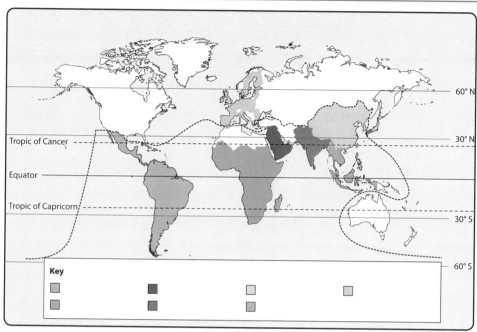

Tropic of Cancer

Equator

Tropic of Capricorn

60° N

30° N

30° S

60° S

**Key**

**3** The seven world regions shown on the world map in **Figure 3** are:

**East Asia;**
**EU;**
**Latin America and the Caribbean;**
**Middle East;**
**South Asia;**
**South East Asia;**
**Sub-Saharan Africa**

**(a)** Complete the map key by naming the world regions shaded on the map.

**Figure 3**  Human distribution – world regions and the North–South wealth divide

**(b)** Study **Figures 1 and 3**. Fill in the table below according to whether the seven world regions contain mainly high or low income countries.

| Mainly high incomes | Mainly low incomes | |
|---|---|---|
| | | |
| | | |
| | | |

# WORLD MAP EXAM PRACTICE

**4** Study **Figure 1** and describe global variations in wealth in relation to

**(a)** latitude

Quick summary of key points ...........................................

....................................................................................

....................................................................................

**(b)** hemisphere

Quick summary of key points ...........................................

....................................................................................

....................................................................................

**(c)** continents and world regions.

Quick summary of key points ...........................................

....................................................................................

....................................................................................

- Start with the highest and lowest values

- Concentrate on where they are found

- Mention also where they are not found

- Round the answer off with a summary comment

For additional guidance, see page 211 of your Understanding Geography textbook.

# GradeStudio

## Guide to answering questions for GCSE exam success

Look back at the Examiner's comments on student answers at the end of each topic, even for those topics you have not studied. What are the main messages about how and how not to answer GCSE exam questions?

| | Do not... | Do... |
|---|---|---|
| **Chapter 8 Population Change (pp. 70–1)** | | |
| Question 1: describing rate of change (not just change in numbers) between two dates from a graph | | |
| Question 2: explaining variations in effectiveness between countries in an answer worth 6 marks | | |
| **Chapter 9 Changing Urban Environments (pp. 78–9)** | Do not... | Do... |
| Question 1: describing characteristics from a photograph | | |
| Question 2: writing a full mark 6 mark answer | | |
| **Chapter 10 Changing Rural Environments (pp. 86–7)** | Do not... | Do... |
| Question 1: describing typical characteristics (of a declining village) | | |
| • content | | |
| • lay out | | |
| **Chapter 11 The Development Gap (pp. 94–5)** | Do not... | Do... |
| Question 2: writing a 6 mark answer with references to physical and human factors | | |
| **Chapter 12 Globalisation (pp. 102–3)** | Do not... | Do... |
| Question 1: describing a distribution from a world map | | |
| Question 2: explaining why some places more than others | | |

| Chapter 13 Tourism (pp. 110–1) | Do not... | Do... |
|---|---|---|
| Question 1: describing evidence for a theme from a photograph | | |
| Question 2: choice of topic in a 6 mark question | | |

## Summary of the main messages

**Describing from photographs**

Do not

Do

**Explaining variations, differences or changes between one place and another.**

Do not

Do

**Writing answers to the longer 6 mark questions**

**(a) Organisation and lay out**

Do not

Do

**(b) Case studies and named examples**

Do not

Do

**(c) Making best use of the space left for answering**

Do not

Do

## Frequently asked questions

**Question:** How do examiners mark the 6 mark questions?

**Question:** How is levels marking different from point marking?

**Answer:** Most questions worth 4 or more marks on Paper 2 are levels marked. In point marking, the examiner gives a tick every time the student makes a point that is in the mark scheme; and then adds up the number of ticks to get the total mark for the question. Whereas with levels marking the examiner reads the whole answer first, and then decides what level has been reached, and what mark it is worth. In this way the examiner checks whether all the requirements for a top Level 3 answer have been met. They are normally looking for things like:

- good content covering all aspects of the question
- precise and relevant information about case study examples
- an answer that is well organised and well written.

# How well did you do?

## Chapter 1 The Restless Earth

### Question 1

☐ Did you state differences between maps A and B?

☐ Did you give more than one difference?

### Question 2

☐ Did you explain fully at least two advantages of living next to an active volcano?

☐ Did you mention a third just to make sure that you claimed all the marks?

☐ Did you refer to an example, such as the area around Mount Vesuvius? This is not essential to gain full marks but referring to a named example always improves answers.

## Chapter 2 Rocks, Resources and Scenery

### Question 1

☐ Did you concentrate not only on observation from the photograph, but also on looking for variations between foreground and background areas?

☐ Did you describe land uses other than just farming, such as trees and their locations and extent?

### Question 2

☐ Did you refer to at least three different rock types in your answer?

☐ Did you describe how farming varied between them?

☐ Did you then try to explain these differences? What did you refer to? Soil, relief and drainage are the main factors that are directly affected by the type of rock.

## Chapter 3 Challenge of Weather and Climate

### Question 1(a)

☐ Did you refer to both temperature and precipitation?

☐ Did you concentrate on looking for the significant data such as highest and lowest temperatures and the seasonal distribution of precipitation?

☐ Did you quote relevant values including units of measurement?

### Question 1(b)

☐ When choosing between latitude and distance from the sea, did you choose the one you understood better and could write most about?

## Chapter 4 Living World

### Question 1(b)

☐ Did you keep your answer local, focused on the area shown in the photograph?

☐ Did you try to give an overview to answer the question posed? For example, how great are the risks of soil erosion here? They are obviously greater than they were when forest protected the surface, but is there still a complete surface cover of vegetation? Are the remaining trees still close enough to offer some shelter against strong winds?

## Question 2

☐ Did you begin by describing the challenges faced by people living in all hot deserts?

☐ Then did you try to show how the challenges were different between deserts in rich and poor parts of the world?

☐ Did you refer to two case study examples to show how and why the challenges are different?

## Chapter 5 Water on the Land

### Question 1(a)(ii)

☐ Did you concentrate only on describing physical features that can be seen on the photograph?

☐ Did you name and describe both river channel and river valley features to show how this is the upper course?

### Question 1(b)

☐ Did you think about other (non-weather) factors which affect river discharge?

☐ These other discharge factors are relief, rock type and land use. Did you concentrate on relief and land use for which the photo evidence is best?

☐ Did you explain how the relief and land uses shown in this area favour rapid runoff into the river in heavy rainfall?

## Chapter 6 Ice on the Land

### Question 1

☐ Did you label the mountain peaks, valley sides and glacier?

☐ Did you concentrate only on describing physical features visible on the photograph without including irrelevant explanation?

### Question 2

☐ Did you refer to at least two different ways for managing the environmental impacts?

☐ Does the case study information directly relate either to environmental impacts, or to ways for reducing them?

## Chapter 7 The Coastal Zone

### Question 1

☐ Did you concentrate on describing only physical features that can be seen on Photograph A?

☐ Did you name and describe landforms other than just the cliffs of soft rock?

### Question 2

☐ Did you explain how rock type and weaknesses lead to rapid cliff collapse along some coasts?

☐ Did you explain more fully how coastal management by people can reduce rates of erosion along some coasts, and increase them along others?

☐ Did you include another example of rapid coastal erosion and explain how rock characteristics and location cause this? Reference to one or even two named examples would be a feature of answers from A* students.

# Chapter 8 Population Change

## Question 1

☐ Did you concentrate on variations in the rate of growth comparing, for example, growth rates before and after 1960?

☐ Did you use (rather than merely repeat) values from the graph, such as the changing number of years for total world population to increase by one billion?

## Question 2

☐ Before starting to write, did you think about factors controlling the effectiveness of a national population policy – such as strength of policy, how vigorously the government supports and promotes it?

☐ Did you refer to the example of more than one country in your answer?

☐ Did you round off your answer off with a general, overall comment about what makes some population policies more effective than others, based upon examples used? This would be a feature of many of the answers from A* grade students.

## Chapter 9 Changing Urban Environments

### Question 1

☐ Did you keep your answer focused on the question by describing housing characteristics only in the area shown on the photograph?

☐ Did you notice how some of the houses in the back of the photograph are different, and then describe how they are different from the others?

## Chapter 10 Changing Rural Environments

### Question 1

☐ Did you think about headings for characteristics before you began to write – such as housing, numbers and types of people, employment, services and the social side of village life?

☐ Did you write about at least three of them, giving a small amount of detail about each one of them?

☐ Did you organise your answer and write in sentences rather than relying on a list?

### Question 2

☐ Before starting to write, did you decide which example or examples of villages you were going to use?

☐ Did you refer to a range of factors for explaining growth or decline?

☐ Did you do anything better than this student? Did you think about rounding off your answer with a summary comment highlighting the most important factors?

# Chapter 11 The Development Gap

## Question 1

The mark for this student was 2/4. Did you identify which of the student's answers were wrong? The correct answers are:

**(a)** Middle East      **(b)** Sub-Saharan Africa      **(c)** South East Asia      **(d)** Middle East

The student's mistakes are:

**(a)** Giving the region with the greatest percentage without access, instead of with access, to safe water in 1975. It's easily done so read the question carefully, and re-read it if necessary.

**(c)** Although South Asia has an equally low percentage in 2005, South East Asia started from a higher percentage in 1975. Its improvement was about 15% greater so its line showing change between the two dates is steeper.

## Question 2

☐ The four groups of factors named in the specification are environmental, economic, social and political. Did you refer to all of these?

☐ Did you keep referring to both rich and poor countries – so that you could bring out the differences (i.e. the gap) between them?

☐ Did you round off your answer with a final comment about why the gap is widening? Did you keep referring to examples in your answer (even though the question does not openly ask for them)? Including these would show the examiner that you are a serious A* grade student.

# Chapter 12 Globalisation

## Question 2

☐ Before starting to write, did you think about a good example of a country that has attracted few (if any) TNCs into it?

☐ Then, when thinking about reasons why, did you try to think of a range of factors – economic, political and social?

☐ Did you round off your answer with a general, overall comment about what makes some countries more favoured than others, perhaps based upon examples used? This would mark you out as a serious A* grade student.

# Chapter 13 Tourism

## Question 1

☐ Did you concentrate on looking at the photograph and describing evidence for mass tourism?

☐ Did you elaborate more fully (i.e. give more details based on describing from the photograph) after identifying the two main pieces of evidence for summer mass tourism?

## Question 2

☐ Before starting to write, did you think about your choice – whether you could write more about a National Park or a coastal resort?

☐ Did you begin by naming the example you were going to use?

☐ Did you refer to names of locations and plans that were specific to your named example? This would be the main distinguishing feature between answers from A* grade students and the rest.

Heinemann is an imprint of Pearson Education Limited, a company incorporated in England and Wales, having its registered office at Edinburgh Gate, Harlow, Essex, CM20 2JE. Registered company number: 872828

www.heinemann.co.uk

Heinemann is a registered trademark of Pearson Education Limited

Text © Pearson Education Limited 2010

First published 2010

14 13 12 11 10

10 9 8 7 6 5 4 3 2 1

British Library Cataloguing in Publication Data

A catalogue record for this book is available from the British Library.

ISBN 978 0 435341 40 4

Designed by Pearson Education Limited

Typeset by Jerry Udall

Original illustrations © Pearson Education Limited 2010

Illustrated by Pearson Education Limited and MW Digital Graphics

Cover design by Pearson Education Limited

Cover photo/illustration © G.M.B. Akash/Panos Pictures

Printed in the UK by Ashford Colour Press

**Acknowledgements**

The authors and publisher would like to thank the following individuals and organisations for permission to reproduce photographs:

p.16 Pearson Education Ltd/John Pallister; pp.32, 40, 48, 56, 78 John Pallister; p.84 Pearson Education Ltd/John Pallister; p.110 John Pallister

The authors and publisher would like to thank the following individuals and organisations for permission to reproduce copyright material:

pp.vi–vii Assessment and Qualifications Alliance – Use of the Trade Mark is under licence from AQA, licence number LAL/14102009121; pp.58, 61 Reproduced by permission of Ordnance Survey on behalf of HMSO. © Crown copyright 2010. All rights reserved. Ordnance Survey Licence number 100030901.

Every effort has been made to contact copyright holders of material reproduced in this book. Any omissions will be rectified in subsequent printings if notice is given to the publishers.